Love Thy Body

Love

UNLEASH

Thy

YOUR

Body

POWER

Laura Bland, Serena Novelli, Ana Bonasera

First published in 2020 by Love Thy Body Project

A CIP catalogue record for this book is available from the British Library

Front and back cover photos by wedding, fashion and boudoir photographer Chantal Storrs-Barbor
www.chantalstorrsbarbor.com

Cover design and typesetting by Fuzzy Flamingo
www.fuzzyflamingo.co.uk

This book is for every woman who has ever felt like she is not enough. It is also for every woman who has ever made a passing comment that she meant with good intention, but which was not received that way.

I see you. I have been you. I have felt like I am not enough.

Know that you are amazing. You are enough and you are loved.

I also dedicate this book to my daughter, Callie, you are my light. I want to make the world a better place for you.

Love always, Laura xx

I dedicate this book to my fiancé Jordan, for always supporting me, being an inspiration through his own career and standing by me through the best of times and the worst.

With Love and Gratitude, Ana xx

I would like to dedicate this book in honour of my beautiful children. Each and every one of you inspire me to make positive changes for this generation and the next.

I am proud of you all. Keep shining and inspiring.

Love Mum (Serena) xx

LAURA BLAND

"The first step is always the hardest, but in buying this book your journey has begun."

Let's Get Real

I am going to start off by being really upfront and pretty blunt with you. In order to find peace with yourself, YOU have to do the work. We can provide support and guidance and show you our own journeys but it is you that will need to delve inside your own thoughts and feelings and start to change the way that you think so that ultimately you can change the way you feel.

The way you think effects the way you feel, the way you feel effects the way you act and the way you act becomes YOUR reality so we have to start the work from inside and then let it shine through.

There is no one single thing that you are going to do that will suddenly allow you to live in a place of self-love and body confidence. This is not as simple as flicking a switch. It is not going to be an easy process and I do not profess to know every trick of the trade, in fact I do not think any of us do, but the beauty of this book is you get the knowledge, experience, and tips from not just one person but from three different women.

We have each been on our own journey, we have

3

had our own battles with our internal demons and somehow, we have come out the other side of it. Not only have we survived our journeys, we have thrived and that is exactly why we are right here sharing those journeys with you. We want you to also find your path and to thrive. Our mission is clear – Empower thousands of women right across the globe to love themselves.

For my part I intend to share with you my own journey, the things I have learnt along the way and some of the tools I use with my own clients. Tools that you can use to take action with, to help you make sense of how you feel and how you want to feel. Tools that I have developed based on my own journey, the research I have done along the way and the things that my clients have responded positively to. By buying this book you have set out in the right direction, you have taken that first giant step towards self-love. I am honoured to be able to support you on your journey. For further support and tips you can also head on over to www.laurab-fitnessmentor.com I promise that although I promote exercise as part of a healthy lifestyle I will not be trying to force you to do anything that you do not want to.

What is Self-love to Me?

What is self-love? That is quite a tricky question to answer and I know that even as we move through this journey together, your definition will be a little different to mine and that is okay. My definition today is vastly different to the definition I would have given just a couple of years ago. This is a journey where we evolve and grow as we move down the path and discover new things about ourselves. Our view of self-love can change and that is a good thing, it is not some unobtainable mystical concept and as you progress through your journey you will come to realise that.

Even though we might all have a different definition for what self-love is I can tell you what I know self-love is not. It is not a certain size or a particular shape, it is not related to age, race, sexuality, or religion. It is not something that only some people are worthy of, but it is something that a lot of us struggle to achieve.

Self-love is one of those terms that we hear all the time now. I imagine that if we went and spoke to our parents and asked them about how self-love was viewed when they were our age or even when they were children the simple answer would be that it was not really talked about or it was not a "thing" the way it is now. It is like a buzz word or phrase that comes in and out of fashion in the office, you hear it nonstop for months and then all of a sudden, poof, it vanishes again.

But self-love, body confidence and self-confidence are not buzz words. They are things that every single one of us deserves to feel every single day. Most of us will start off in life with no concept of what any of these are, we just live in the moment enjoying ourselves, and yet as children we often have all three, and in abundance! It is only as we move through life, interact with different people and have different experiences that we start to take knocks and then question ourselves.

If you had asked me even just a couple of years ago about self-love and whether I had it, I would have scoffed at you. I literally would have laughed out loud. I had in my mind that self-love meant that you were perfect or that you at least thought you were perfect and that was something I was never going to be!

Yet over the last couple of years I have come to realise that self-love and body confidence have nothing at all to do with being perfect, or at least not the kind of perfect that I had imagined it to be.

To me self-love is about self-respect, acceptance, self-care, and forgiveness.

So What Goes Wrong?

Our toddler self has no concept that another child might be viewed by some as "prettier", more "feminine", more "able", more "advanced" in their abilities, more "confident" etc. As a toddler we just exist, we attempt to do the things that we want to do, keeping our parents on their toes, we eat the foods we like, spit out the ones we do not, and when we fall down we get back up again. We do not easily give up.

As we grow, as we move through childhood, into adolescence and then into our young adult years we take in millions of pieces of information, have thousands of interactions and experiences and we form different views of our surroundings, the people we interact with, and, most importantly, ourselves.

Unfortunately, not every interaction or experience we have is a positive one. Maybe as a child we are teased by family or peers and told we are "chubby" or "skinny" or have a "boyish" figure, perhaps a boyfriend says hurtful things to us or treats us badly, maybe we suffer mental or physical abuse at the hands of those who should be caring for us and nurturing us, perhaps we never get picked for the lead in the school play, maybe our body is a different size or shape to our friends, or we develop early on, or it seems like we do not develop at all, maybe we get teased in what is meant to be a harmless way but which knocks us down. Maybe a thousand other things happen.

We carry all of these experiences with us. Some we forget. Some we can brush off and just move past. Some make us pause and wonder "why me" and then there are those experiences that stay with us long after the event. The experiences that lead to ingrained feelings and behaviours, that lead us to think we are not "enough". Not good enough, not pretty enough, not slim enough, not tall enough, not smart enough, not confident enough, the list goes on but essentially, we feel we are just not enough!

If we are not enough then how do we find self-love? This is where some of those things that I mentioned before – self-respect, forgiveness, and self-care – come into play.

Forgiveness

When I talk of forgiveness I do not just mean forgiving those that have done us wrong in the past. Don't get me wrong that is an important part of the process, being able to work through past issues and forgive others is a very cathartic process and means we carry much less negativity with us. The more important part though, at least in my opinion, is learning to forgive ourselves. This can be really hard to do; it can take a lot of work and in finding what we need to forgive we can unearth some not so pleasant things that have been buried.

You might be thinking right now that you have nothing to forgive yourself for, perhaps you feel like you have been a victim at the hands of others; and that may be true, but you will see as we move forward that we are often our own worst enemy and this is something we have to work hard on to change. Once we create that change though there is no going back, and you will not regret it.

Forgiveness could be your first step on the ladder to self-love.

The first thing we need to do is start with our own thoughts, we need to get hold of that naughty little voice that whispers in our ear and tries to hold us back. We all have it, even the most positive and confident people that you can think of will have that voice that tries to whisper poison to them. It is only as we learn to hear it for what it really is – our own fear and insecurities – that we can start to get control of it. As we gain control, we can change the narrative and lead a more fulfilled life. A life where we are truly in charge and living to the fullest that we can.

Start to forgive yourself for all the mean things you say to yourself, I know that you do it. I know you talk down to yourself and you talk yourself out of doing things because you feel you are "not enough". I know because that was absolutely me. Working on my own internal negative voice was one of the first things I did as I worked towards self-love. Even now when I am much further along on my own journey, I still have to battle those thoughts, flip those negatives around and sometimes forgive myself.

That naughty little negative voice can follow us around and hound us day and night. It can hold us back and stop us from doing truly amazing things. It can bully us relentlessly and leave us feeling angry, sad, low, and maybe even vulnerable. Sometimes that voice speaks to us over the smallest of things, but it still makes us doubt ourselves.

It is important that we understand that we all have up days and down days, that sometimes we will feel energised, positive, and ready to take on the world and other days we will want to pull the duvet over our heads and just ignore the world. That is okay and it is perfectly normal to experience these ups and downs. What we do want to do though is find what brings the downs, if we can begin to understand what makes us have those low days then we can work on minimising those and at the same time create more of the ups.

Forgiveness can help us to shake off those downs and start to see a more positive way forward. Love is an incredibly powerful, uplifting, and positive emotion, but we need to learn how to harness it in the right way. Love itself is not damaging but there can be many times that it is abused and used in the wrong way and in those cases, it can become toxic and harmful. The more positive emotions we can bring into our day and our daily routines the more success we are going to have and the quicker we are going to move forward.

I've had to work on a lot of internal forgiveness, and unfortunately it is not an overnight process. I didn't even really know what I was doing when I first got started or where it would lead me but I knew I wanted to be a better version of myself and for that I needed to do things differently. Keep in mind the brilliant quote from Mark Twain "If you do what you have always done, then you will get what you have always got". Change is where the magic happens.

Each one of us will find self-love in a different place both physically, spiritually, and mentally. There is no "one size fits all" when it comes to self-love and those that try to tell you there is are kidding you; and quite possibly themselves. This is a journey I can help to guide you on, I can share with you my journey and my tips but ultimately the path you will follow is your own. My aim is that you reach your destination and that you can smile, love, laugh and possibly cry along the way.

How My Journey Began

My journey began in earnest when I realised that I had been habitually trying to change myself in order to please others. One of the biggest examples I can give you of that goes right back to 2007, to when I was twenty-six years old, single, and watching my friends settle down one by one. My goal was to take up running, GET FIT and LOSE WEIGHT and THEN I would MEET A MAN. Let me say that again; LOSE WEIGHT and THEN I would MEET A MAN. I remember saying this plan out loud on more than one occasion and to more than one person. Was I nuts???

Here I was at twenty-six thinking that I was not worthy, that I was fat and that this was why I was single and had not found love. I mean, really!?! I look back on this and I can see how crazy it was but at the time I honestly felt this way. I felt that I had to lose weight to be worthy of love, and until it happened, I would not meet anyone.

Now if my best friend had come to me and said these things about herself I would have told her straight the way that she was being ridiculous, that she was beautiful, funny, smart and that any man would

13

be lucky to have her just the way she was. Yet I could not tell myself these things. At the time I didn't give it a second thought, I had no clue just how much I was beating myself down. My plan felt perfectly normal and natural.

I am not sure where this feeling came from but when I looked in the mirror, I did not see someone who was worthy of love and all the wonderful things that being in love would bring. The adventures, the firsts, the memory making, the planning for the future. Nope I was fat, so it wasn't going to happen.

I honestly felt that this was my reality, in truth I was never more than a size sixteen to eighteen in UK clothes sizes and although that was bigger than my pre-university size twelve it still wasn't that big and even if it was; why should that matter? Even if I had been a size thirty or a size four why should that have mattered? Why should the number in my clothes dictate the level of happiness I could expect? Before we carry on and go any further together it is important to me that you know right now that size does not matter, the number on the scale does not matter. You deserve love and happiness and it has nothing whatsoever to do with either of these things.

It took years for me to realise just how foolish those thoughts had been. I'd say it was probably as late as 2014 before I started to see how damaging my thoughts had been and how they had unwittingly held me back. The catalyst for making me realise my mindset was part of the issue was having my daughter. She was born in the summer of 2012, I fell in love immediately and I knew that I wanted her to love, respect, and honour herself no matter what. For that I needed to be a great role model.

ACTIVITY ONE

Remember, in order to move forward you have to do the work, so do not just skip over the activities we include. You have taken the first step in investing in your future relationship with yourself by buying this book so now invest some time in doing the activities we give you; I promise they will help.

I am going to ask you to keep a diary for the next five days.

In it write down all the negative little thoughts you have.

This dress is too tight, this colour is too bright, I shouldn't speak up, no one wants to hear my opinion, my friends don't really like me, I am not a good cook, I do not deserve the promotion, she's a better wife/ mum/friend/daughter/sister than me, I wish I was as good as her, I wish I looked like she does, that would never work for me, why does nothing ever go right, my arms are fat, my bum is big, I hate my mum tum, I'm too short, I'm too skinny, …

Every negative thought big or small just write it down.

I know it might feel painful to see it there in black

and white and I know that it might make you feel a little sad, but we need to get these thoughts out. We need to openly admit them to our self and allow them to affect us so that ultimately, we can start to get rid of them. Trust me on this.

Now write a letter to yourself but speak as you would to a best friend and tell yourself how amazing and wonderful you really are.

Squash each of those negative things you wrote down. Write with love, understanding and positivity.

This might feel as hard as it did to read back all of those negative things you have been saying but just keep remembering that you are writing as you would to your best friend. Your job in this letter is to uplift, support and nurture.

Pop that letter somewhere safe, you are going to read it over and over to remind yourself that those negative thoughts are just in your head, they do not own you, they do not define you and no one else is thinking those things about you.

The next time you are having a bad day instead of reaching for the negative thoughts reach for the letter you wrote and remind yourself that you are incredible.

The Turning Point

Having my daughter in the summer of 2012 started my new journey, it was a long and slow process and back in those early days I had no label for it. I didn't know that what I was looking for was self-love or self-acceptance or body confidence. What I knew was that I wanted to be fit, strong, and healthy and I wanted to be a good role model.

I did what so many new mums do in the beginning, I criticised myself for not losing the baby weight fast enough. My reality was twisted but I had no idea. I lacked the right kind of motivation and understanding to find the healthy version of myself.

Not long after our daughter was born my partner found himself no longer able to go to work. He was facing a series of physical challenges that went on to alter the course of our lives completely. What it also did was alter the path of my maternity leave and the time that I had at home with my beautiful new baby. Now I am not going to say that things would have been better without the challenges we faced but they certainly would have been different. I felt torn in so many different directions that it was impossible to make myself a priority, but with a new baby at home I doubt that would have happened anyway.

As time progressed, I found myself not just trying to meet the needs of my new-born but also trying to meet the increasing needs of my partner. What he was going through dragged him down into the depths of despair and depression; and ultimately he took me part of the way down with him. There were times when I felt like a single parent, struggling on my own, at other times it felt like I had two children to care for, but then there would also be the times where life felt amazing. I was uplifted, happy, in a little bubble with my little family. It was quite the roller coaster.

We rode that roller coaster round and round, up and down, for several years before it finally seemed that we were able to get off of it and actually move forward. We still have our ups and downs and with the nature of my partners physical disability I think we always will but it is no longer the full-blown scary ride that it used to be.

During the lows I became a secret emotional eater. I would binge eat in the evenings when there was no one around to see or question what I was doing. I was satisfying my emotions with bars of chocolate, packs of biscuits and who knows how many bags of crisps. In what were our hardest times I turned inwards. Rather than reaching out for help I bottled all of my emotions up, put on a brave face and coined the phrase "It's just life, so we have to get on with it".

No one asked me to keep things to myself, no one told me that I was dragging them down or that they were fed up of listening to my problems. In my own head I felt that if I talked about the negatives too much then my friends wouldn't like me or want to be around me. I thought that if I talked about how hard things sometimes felt that my friends would judge us, and my partner in particular.

I realise now just how foolish I was but at the time I was doing what I thought was right to protect myself and my little family. You see those doubts I had, those negative thoughts in my head, they were really taking hold and they were ruling so many aspects of my life. Even now I sometimes hold back from talking about what is going on because I do not want to feel judged or have people feel sorry for me, I do not want to feel weak. This is an area that I am still working on changing, I am still learning to just be me as much and as often as I can be.

Being an emotional eater and bottling my emotions up led me down the path of weight gain, of feeling sluggish, bloated and just downright unhealthy, of not loving the person that looked back at me from the mirror. The realisation that I needed to be more and do better for my daughter was the best thing that could have happened to me.

My Journey with Exercise

When I was in my teens I rode my bike every week, I loved horse riding and helping out at the stables, I would spend all of my time outdoors, and I even took up learning Karate during my first two years at university. What all of these had in common was that I genuinely enjoyed doing them and I did them for pleasure, just for me, no other reason. Up until my early twenties, exercise was just the by-product of doing the things I loved and because I loved them, I did lots of them and had no problem at all staying in shape.

When I think now of how I would spend my childhood summers I smile at memories of spending countless hours outdoors with friends; come rain or shine. When I think about our children today and all the technology and gadgets available to them it is no wonder that they spend less time playing, running around, and using their imagination and more time stuck inside. The statistics on childhood obesity scare me, but that is a topic for another book.

Before I became body conscious or self-critical, I was active purely for enjoyment. It was not about losing weight or fitting into a certain outfit and it certainly was not about meeting Mr Right. It was just about fun. It was about spending time with my friends. It was about being at the stables and doing something that made me happy. From grooming the horses to mucking out the stables, to riding, to helping the little kids learn to ride. Everything was about enjoyment.

By the time I finished university a lot of that had changed, I was no longer horse riding, I had quit Karate and I had not been on my bike in far too long. I was excited to get my first real job, I remember feeling so grown up and mature when in reality it was the equivalent of a basic administration job in an office and had nothing at all to do with the degree that I'd just worked so hard to get. I went out shopping for some new clothes for work and was surprised, and not in a good way, at the size I had to buy.

Later that year I got what I am sure was a well-meaning gift but what felt like a kick in the stomach to me. This was the start of me using exercise not because I enjoyed it but because I felt I had to do it to lose weight.

I received an exercise bike. I do not remember ever having asked for one but maybe that is part of the past I've blocked out? Maybe it was something that I really wanted but because I did not want to admit how I felt about myself and how much my health had slipped, it is something that I've pushed aside and blocked from memory. As I look back now though it felt like I was being told I was fat, lazy, and unworthy. I am not sure now though where it came from, and the more I think about it the more I wonder if I was saying those things to myself.

Our minds are incredible and part of what they do every single day is block out the things that will hurt us the most, we supress so many memories, thoughts, and feelings. It really is incredible but doesn't always do us any good. Maybe I bought that bike myself but over time my memory has distorted, and I've subconsciously told myself a different story to protect myself. That is a sad thought in itself.

I rode that bike for hours at a time. I would sit and read a book and just peddle away. It was ridiculous really. I had no idea what I was doing in regard to a fitness plan, so I was not riding with any structure or in a way that really challenged me. I was just peddling. It did the job and I eventually lost the weight but there was no enjoyment in what I was doing. I felt like it had not been my choice and that this was something I had to do.

ACTIVITY TWO

It is time to start thinking about your own relationship with exercise.

Over the next five days keep a note of any exercise that you do and write down:

- How you feel before you start
- How you feel whilst exercising
- How you feel once done
- How long you exercised for
- What activity you did
- Why you chose that activity

Exercising can and should be enjoyable, but we often pick the wrong reasons to start or the wrong activity to do.

At the end of the five days have a look at the notes you made:

- Did you do any real exercise? By this I mean something purposeful that you set out to do on purpose.
- Did you enjoy it?

- What activities did you enjoy the most?
- How did you feel each time before you started? Were you looking forward to it? Were you doing it because you felt you "had" to?
- How did you feel once you finished? Did you have a sense of accomplishment? Did you hate it and just want it to be over as soon as possible?

Look for as many positives as you can.

A sense of achievement can lift your mood and leave you feeling more positive for the rest of the day.

An activity that you enjoyed will have you ready to do it again.

Even if you didn't love it getting your heart rate up is incredibly good for your physical fitness, not to mention how being active can support your mental health.

But the big one is WHY – WHY are you choosing to exercise? WHY did you choose those activities?

If the answer is because you feel like you "have to" or you "should do" or you are doing it to "change" for someone else then the chances are it is going to feel like a form of punishment; just like that exercise bike did for me and you simply will not enjoy it or stick with it.

Do not worry though as we are going to look more at exercise later and how we can turn it into something good, something that we do FOR OURSELVES and no one else.

Self-Respect and Self-Care

I mentioned right at the start that for me these two things, self-respect and self-care, form part of self-love and actually they form a significant part. If we love our body then we are more likely to treat it with respect, and if we respect our body then we are more likely to love it. Can you see how they fit together? The same is true for self-care, an act of self-care means showing our mind or body love.

These three elements are not mutually exclusive, they are intertwined and go hand in hand in many ways. You may not have all three right now but where there is one there is usually a second or at least you are on the path to achieving a second.

So, if these elements are intertwined it makes sense that we can work on them as individual entities and naturally increase the other elements around it. For example, an act of self-care is really an act of love and kindness towards our self so can also be seen as increasing and reinforcing our self-love.

Self-care is another of those terms that is banded around everywhere that you look at the minute. Social media is full of "Self-care Sunday" posts, there are thousands of blogs you can read about self-care and what it should look like or what it should involve and we are told now that without some form of self-care we are all going to burn out and then end up miserable. Is that really the case?

What is all the fuss about? What is self-care? How do I incorporate self-care into an already busy life? Is it something I have to do daily? Will it take hours? How will I know when I have done enough of it? Is it going to cost me lots? These are just a few of the questions I've asked myself so I can imagine you might be asking them too.

This is another one of those areas where we all have a slightly different answer and the reason for that is in the name – SELF-care. That means it is something for each of us that connects directly with our self. Your form of self-care may not be the same as what I like or what Doris down the road likes and that is the whole point. Self-care is anything at all that makes you feel grounded, energised, happy, rested, fulfilled, renewed, alive... Self-care is just something that YOU do for YOU because YOU want to and that means it can take many different forms.

My favourite forms of self-care are:

- Exercise – I love to get out running, it gives me time in my own head space to think things through or I can just completely switch off and focus only on how my body is moving.
- Bubble baths and a book – I love to relax in the bath

with a good romance novel or thriller, though this is something I rarely find the time for.

- Jigsaw Puzzles – I don't know where it came from really – actually that is a lie, about 5 years ago my next-door neighbour bought my partner a jigsaw to do whilst he was recovering from an operation. It was seriously hard and frustrated the heck out of him so me and my other next-door neighbour completed it instead over many nights of girl talk and bottles of wine and I fell in love with doing them.
- Writing – just like I am doing now I love to write because I like to be creative and it is also such a cathartic process at times.
- A hot cup of tea and 5 minutes peace – this is the one I try to get most days!!
- A day at the spa – by far my favourite and a real luxury and one I combine as a girl's day out. What could be better than spending the day relaxing, having some girl talk and getting a massage?
- Reading – I love to get lost in a good book, to allow my imagination to just run away with the characters.

There are a real range of things here that I love and class as self-care, some take 5 minutes and cost next to nothing and others take a whole day and make a significant dent in my purse. Every single one is a valid form of self-care for me because I enjoy them all and I do them for me and not because I have to or because someone told me. What will your self-care activity be?

Mindset and Language

As I moved forward in my journey, and particularly as my daughter started to grow and pick up on what I was saying and how I was acting, I knew that more than just what I ate or how much I exercised had to change. I also needed to work on my mindset and on the language that I used.

I grew up in a loving home, mum, dad, my sister, and me. We weren't well off, but we also never went without. I have lots of incredibly happy memories from my childhood, but I also have memories of words like "fat", "diet", and "junk food" being used in our house. Not, I hasten to add, when talking about each other, but definitely in regard to how my mum would talk about herself.

Of course, I know now that we should talk to ourselves in much kinder ways and with words that lift us up rather than knock us down but even just thirty-five years ago as I was growing up it was a completely different story. The world was not as switched on to things like 'positivity', 'empowerment', 'body confidence' or the way our words shape our reality in the way that it is now.

The world has changed and adapted and many of us have had to run to catch up. As my daughter grew and was learning to talk and to understand the world around her I knew that it was my job to ensure that we had conversations that reflected the love I wanted her to always have for herself. That meant that I needed to shift the way I thought and spoke, I needed to either remove certain words and phrases from my vocabulary or I needed to ensure they adopted a new meaning.

That desire to be the best version of myself to be a role model for my daughter helped me. It started the process of my shift in mindset and it forms the starting point of what I work on with coaching clients. My clients might come to me for help with fitness and maybe ultimately weight loss but the first thing we work on is mindset, the language we use, and the way we view ourselves.

If you cannot love and appreciate your body for what it is then will any level of fitness or any amount of weight loss ever really make you happy? Stop and think about that for a minute, really think about it. The answer is most likely no, sure getting fitter is definitely worth the effort and weight loss, if it is going to benefit your health, can be a good thing but are they alone the answer to finding self-love and happiness?

I started to think about the things I would say in front of my daughter, I tried very hard not to say things like how I was fat or I felt fat or that an outfit made me look fat. In fact, I tried not to say the word fat at all. I stopped talking about diets and weight loss and instead rephrased things. When she was little I would talk to her about yummy foods that tasted nice but did not help our bodies grow big and strong so we only had them as nice treats every so often, and then I would talk about yummy healthy food that our body could break down into little bits and use to grow strong.

I have tried to make sure that it has not been about good food versus bad food, healthy food versus unhealthy food. I have made a conscious choice to teach her that all food is okay and can be enjoyed but that some foods serve us better than others.

I wanted my daughter to know that food was fuel and was designed to keep her body strong and healthy but that all food could be eaten and enjoyed. We just need to remember that some food choices are better for our bodies than others. My hope with this was that she would not become the secret binge eater that I used to be. I do not want her to use food as a form of punishment by either overeating or by denying herself the food that her body needs. I felt that if she could make healthy choices from a young age and she had positive reasons for those choices; rather than fearing the choices she was making, then that would be a much healthier mindset for her to be in.

This shift in the language I was using internally and externally started to make a difference. I started to feel more positive about myself, surer of the choices I was making and that had a compound effect making those healthy positive choices easier each time I came to a crossroads.

I still have to work at the language I use, those words of negativity still exist, I've just got really good at choosing to ignore them and to look for more positive words instead.

Looking in the mirror or at photographs used to be one of my biggest triggers and in some ways still is. As I look back and reflect on how I used to behave I can see that one of two things would happen, I would either ignore the mirror for weeks at a time and not look in it or I would stand in front of the mirror and critique my body. My tummy wasn't flat enough, my arms were big and wobbly, my thighs were fat and rubbed together, my boobs were saggy, my nose was too big, was hair was plain etc. The list seemed never ending. I needed to change that dialogue, I had to find the positives in the body that I had.

Now when I get triggered, which I still do from time to time, I come back to those positives I found. When the negative thoughts creep in I flip the script and I come back to the thoughts and the truths that can help and support me. I purposely remind myself of all the good points even though it took a while in the beginning for me to believe them.

I remember asking someone once "When do you start to believe it? At what point do you say something positive to yourself and not have your mind immediately say – "yes but that's lie, you're just trying to trick yourself, you don't really believe that". I wanted to know at what point that would change. The only answer that I got was that it takes time and she was right, it does take time, but it is time well spent.

Time for you to work on finding the positives.

ACTIVITY THREE

It is time to stand in front of a mirror and look at yourself, and I mean really look at yourself. Write down all the things you do not like about your body and the way you look.

If you want to you can draw a stick figure in the middle of your page and then write everything down around it.

Get it all out on paper – the wrinkles you do not like, the chubby arms, the thighs that rub together, the hip bones that protrude too far, the nose that is too big, the feet that are too small, the stubby chubby fingers you have (those are mine), the knobbly knees, the saggy bottom, the too round bottom, the boyish figure, the stretch marks…

Write it all down.

Take a look at what you have written and pick the one area that bothers you the most, now write down 3 positive things about that area.

For example

• Those wrinkles on your face are a sign of many happy times spent laughing with friends.

- The stretch marks you have could be a sign of your body creating another human life
- The fact that you are taller than your friends means you can see over the crowd when you are out

My biggest hang up is my upper arms. To me they are large and flabby, sometimes they feel uncomfortable in my clothes, short sleeves can be tight and pinch, but no sleeves means everyone can see how big they are, and long sleeves feel claustrophobic.

So, I need my magic three, I need those positives that I can come back to when that naughty voice starts to whisper in my ear about how awful my arms are.

My magic three

- My arms allow me to hold my daughter close, to show her I love her and to comfort her if she is sad
- My arms allow me to carry the shopping I have bought that will feed my family
- My arms may be a bit too wobbly, but they have a hidden strength and I know I can count on them

What will your magic three be? Once you have found them for that one key thing that you really dislike the most, move onto the next thing and then the next and the next. If you cannot think of three positive things make sure you find at least one for every item you wrote down.

Write all those positive things out on a new clean

sheet of paper. If you can then make it a nice big sheet and spread them out, decorate that paper with things that make you smile. Maybe you draw some love hearts, some flowers, some smiley faces, whatever makes you smile. This is like our mini mood board, it is something tangible for you to look at and read on those days when you are struggling.

Keep your magic three about all those areas in a safe place in your mind and when those thoughts of doubt creep in, pull them out.

I saw a photo of myself on social media not too long ago that made me reach for my magic three. I was on holiday at a party with friends and had a huge smile on my face, I was having a great time BUT I was wearing a bikini and I had both of my arms up in the air. My eyes were immediately drawn to my arms, not the smile on my face, not the fact that I was having a great time. What I saw and registered first was my arms and the thought of "of my gosh they are so big, why did I wear that? I look awful"

I had to get my magic three out – my arms are strong, my arms let me hold and comfort my daughter, my arms help me carry the shopping to feed my family. I repeated these to myself and then I was able to look at the picture and actually enjoy what I was seeing and remember how good I was feeling in that moment.

Yes, those naughty thoughts had been triggered in my mind but I had been able to flip the script and push them aside so that I could feel the positive emotions and not let those other feelings spoil the memories that I had made.

Finding your magic three does not mean that the voice of doom doesn't surface and whisper those naughty words to you. Finding your magic three does mean that you are armed and able to shake the negatives aside and move forward with positivity and love.

The more you practice using your magic three the more you will believe them, the more you will trust your own words and the quieter that naughty voice in your head will become.

Our Emotions

It is not just the language about ourselves and the way we see food that we need to change it is also the connotations and feelings that we have attached to certain words over time that we also need to work on changing.

Some words have the ability to trigger a strong emotional response the moment we hear them, and it is not always the kind of response that is working in our favour. Some words can have an extremely negative impact on us, they can evoke feelings of dread, anticipation of failure and all sorts of other emotions that do not help us to move forward.

For example, if I said the word 'diet' to you what kinds of images, emotions, and words come to mind? I can guess it is something like the following:

- Restrictive
- Boring
- Rabbit food
- Expensive
- Hard work
- No enjoyment

- Can't eat out
- Can't have takeaway
- Tasteless
- Yoyo
- Not worth it
- Never works

They are all fairly negative words or conjure up a negative association. Now what if I said you could eat anything at all, that what you ate would have no negative impact on your heath, your body, your self-image, the way other people view you or anything else. What words come to mind then:

- Freedom
- Enjoyable
- Social
- Delicious
- Luxury
- Fun
- Easy

We have a much more positive set of words, words that have the power to make us smile. So, what if I now told you that the word 'diet' is not negative at all. That the word itself merely refers to the foods you choose to eat regardless of what they are and whether or not they are deemed as healthy. Sometimes we have to go right back to basics, re-evaluate what a word means and how we should be feeling. So, lets do that.

Part of my journey has been stripping back to basics and looking at things from a new perspective. When you start to do that you can start to shift your mindset and we already know that mindset is key. Start working on that change as you look at food.

All food will serve a purpose, but many foods will nourish your body and provide it with fuel in a way that other foods will not. If you don't currently have a great relationship with food, then here are a couple of little tricks you can use.

If you know that you tend to overeat and have portion sizes that are just too big even if it is a really healthy food choice, then try eating from a smaller plate.

- If you reduce your portion size but eat from your normal plate the mind can play tricks on you. You take in that your plate looks half empty and your brain assumes that you will be left feeling hungry and dissatisfied. Guess what – you end up feeling hungry and dissatisfied. So, trick your brain, use a smaller plate and it will still look full even though you have chosen to have a smaller portion.

If you know that your food choices are not always very healthy and you want to change that so you can feel more energised and vibrant, then instead of focussing on cutting out certain foods focus on adding the healthy foods in.

- This is the crowding out method and basically works on the principle that if you are eating more of the healthy foods you will have less time, desire, and hunger for the unhealthy foods.
- Setting out with denial and restriction in mind can often end in failure and a tendency to then binge on the very foods you have been trying to avoid. Using the crowding out method instead of straight denial can help to reduce the chances of these binge tendencies.

If you know that you punish yourself by not allowing yourself to eat, if you regularly skip meals, or eat such a low calorie count that your body and your mental health is suffering then your focus, along with potentially seeking guidance from a professional, could be to add one extra small meal into your day. Don't set out to go from 600 calories a day to 1500 in a single leap as I am sure that is just as hard physically and mentally as making such a big cut would be.

- Instead of a big change look for one small thing that you could change, one extra item that you could eat each day without causing yourself stress and anxiety. When that one small extra item becomes normal add another item in.

I am not a qualified eating disorder expert, please seek medical/professional help and advice if you are struggling either to cut down or build back up and if your health is at risk.

Food is not something that we should use to punish ourselves with either by withholding it or by bingeing on it. Many of us have a complex relationship with food and starting to understand our own behaviours, our thoughts, our feelings, and our triggers can help us to move into a healthier space and relationship with food.

Let's Talk Fitness and Exercise.

You name it and I have done it! I've been the girl at the gym before and after work. I've been the one up at the crack of dawn to get to the swimming pool and get in a mile before work. I've been the one doing 2 or even 3 group classes back to back in one evening (where did I even get the energy for that???). I have been the runner, the walker, the cyclist. I have done exercise because I loved it, and I have done exercise because I felt like I "should".

Whilst the physical act of moving and being fit has always had positive benefits in many ways, there have also been times when that exercise has been detrimental to my health. I have never been one to push through when I am injured but I have been to the gym plenty of times when actually I was ill and should have been home resting.

What drove me to the gym on the occasions when I knew that I really should be at home was this fear that if I missed even just that one workout then everything else I had done that week would have been for nothing.

Missing that one workout would leave me overweight. Missing that one workout would mean I would not hit my fitness goals. Missing that one workout would somehow have a catastrophic effect.

Of course, I know that all of that sounds ridiculous and I know now that it was ridiculous but at the time that was how I actually felt. Fortunately, it was only a short period of time that I let these feelings rule me. I do not even want to begin to think where I might be now if I had continued to push myself and let these foolish fears take control.

Even when I had a much healthier relationship with exercise I still thought that in order for a workout to be effective you had to be pushing to your limit all the time, working up a sweat and spending at least an hour at it. I have come to have a very different view now and it has been one of the biggest things to give me back my love of exercising for all of the right reasons.

I saw a personal trainer for a while when I wanted to get back a part of who I was before I'd had my daughter. I wanted to do something for me, I wanted to have some time where I could be focused just on who I was. At times I felt like I was being selfish, but I also knew that for me this was a form of self-care and would help me to de-stress and recharge.

I got fitter and I hit my goal weight, I changed some of my eating habits for much healthier ways and I was definitely benefitting from doing something that was just for me but I did not automatically love myself. I felt healthier and more positive in many ways and it is true that some of the mean things I had been saying to myself had changed but I was still plagued with doubt and self-criticism. What I thought would be the answer – weight loss – really was not.

Seeing the PT did do lot of good things for me though. My relationship with food had started to change, I realised that a lot of the foods I was eating actually caused an inflammatory reaction in my body. Until I cut out certain foods, I had no idea that how I physically felt was not the way I should feel. Until I stopped eating refined white pasta and refined white bread, I did not realise that the feeling of bloating and how my stomach would swell and ache almost immediately after eating them wasn't normal.

There are lots of foods that I love but which do not love me, but until I saw the PT and I started to look at my food more closely I just had no clue what they were doing to me. My eating habits are not always on point, I try to live in balance which for me means foods that are good for me 80-90% of the time and treats the other 10-20%

A tired bloated sluggish feeling after eating is not normal and if that is the way you are often left feeling please do not just accept it. Do some work to eliminate the major allergens from your everyday diet and then see how you feel. Then as you reintroduce those foods see again how you feel and what the difference is – you might be left surprised.

Probably one of the biggest learnings I had from my time with the PT was that I was able to exercise effectively to improve my fitness without it having to take hours and hours and hours and hours and even more hours. I was able to do the forms of exercise that I loved in a way that fit my life and as well as helping my physical fitness I also noticed a change in my mental health.

My sessions with the PT were never more than forty-five minutes long, in fact they were normally closer to thirty minutes. The sessions were enjoyable, I got fitter, stronger and leaner and I felt more positive about all sorts of things. It wasn't just that physically I was changing it was that I knew I could commit to myself, to my goals, to my health.

I was realising that if I focused on actions and activities that felt good and that fit with my lifestyle then I was more likely to be able to maintain them and see long lasting benefits. I think it was way back in 2014 when I first saw that PT, three years later I was still exercising consistently, but in my own home.

My life took a bit of a crazy and unexpected turn due to an injury and a subsequent life changing operation that my partner went through. My days of getting out to the gym became a distant memory. When I took the jump and started seeing the PT it was not straight forward or simple. I could not just head out the door and leave my eighteen-month-old with my partner as sometimes he was physically unable to look after her. I would often rope my dad in to help us out.

Seeing a PT was not sustainable at that time, either financially or with our home circumstances, but that was okay because he had played a major role in the start of my journey. He had shown me to look at food differently and he had given me back my love of exercise and of doing it for me.

Regular exercise was so good for my mental health and for giving me some much-needed time to myself, so it was not something that I was going to give up, I just needed a different way of doing it. I lost my way again for a while, but I soon found my footing and I got back out running then I eventually started working out at home in our living room and that is when the magic started to happen.

To this day, years later I still aim for workouts under forty-five minutes long and I still workout at home, though I have progressed from the living room to our garage. I shout about home workouts because regular exercise gives you so many positives and so many of us cannot get to a gym, cannot afford a gym, or just do not like the gym. So, my final challenge to you is to get up and get moving, you do not need to buy expensive kit, you do not even need to leave the house. I can promise you though that once you get started you will see multiple benefits to regular exercise.

I created my business in order to support other women that had been struggling just like me. I took all the different elements I had learned on my own journey up to that point, like goal setting, mindset, self-care, nutrition, exercise, my new definition of self-love, and I combined them to help other women find the way on their own journey. I have never been one to focus on weight loss with my clients instead I've helped them to focus on health, happiness and body confidence, for me those are much more important things than the number on the scale. Those are the things I want you to focus on too.

Final Thoughts

You are more than the number on the scale. You are more than the number in your clothes. No number should ever be able to define you. You have the power to change how you view yourself. It can feel like an overwhelming process with so many different elements that link together but once you get started, and working through the activities in the book and reading our journey is a great way to start, you will find that the benefits soon start to show.

You will often hear me say that if it does not challenge you then it will not change you and that is one hundred percent true whether it is stepping outside of your comfort zone, saying no to a slice of cake, or setting your alarm so you can get up and work out. When you feel the challenge that is the time to step up, stand tall and really go for it.

I did not get it right to begin with, remember I said I had no idea what I was doing or what it was that I was looking for at the beginning. Well, although I took a wrong turn or two, my journey has still led me to where I am today and for that I am blessed. I am grateful to have travelled my own journey to find self-love and body confidence as it is now allowing me to help you to do exactly the same.

However you found this book, whether you are part of my community, Fitness and Self Love with Laura B Fitness Mentor, on Facebook, or you are part of our Love Thy Body Project community I am grateful to have you here and to be able to support you.

Author, speaker and cheer leader for women all across the globe, Laura, is a mum of one and knows first-hand how easy it is to put yourself last.

Laura's mission is to help thousands of women awaken and realise that they are beautiful just as they are, that exercise goes far beyond the physical and that self-love does not mean feeling like you are perfect.

Her business focusses on realistic and fun approaches to fitness and a healthy well rounded lifestyle approach incorporating mindset and body confidence alongside exercise and nutrition.

You can find out more about what Laura does and how you can work with her at

www.laurab-fitnessmentor.com and of course you can get involved with Love Thy Body Project at www. lovethybodyproject.com

ANA LOUISE BONASERA

"If man can go to the moon, you can learn to love the skin you're in."

What is Self-Love?

"When did you decide to change, what moment did you decide to love yourself?" A man from BBC Radio Oxford asked as a camera pointed directly at me in the middle of my living room. I was sitting on my sofa, which had been moved from its usual spot against our chalk board wall to reveal an array of toys, dust, and rubbish, with four kids I expected more to be honest. I laughed inside, *such a strange question, just one moment?!* However, it was not the first time I'd been asked this (and it wouldn't be the last) but it was probably the first time I contemplated when I began to question.

Now, before we get into my story, I want to explain to you how I see self-love. You see everyone has a different take on what the definition of self-love is, and I actually find it fascinating to hear other people's interpretations. This is how I would define self-love…

Self-love: a life path a person chooses, to go against the current in the waters, to turn off the negative demon in their head feeding them negative stories, and step into their true selves through finding clarity of who they are, what they love, and shining from the inside out. Self-love has no end destination. It is a constant journey but there are ways we can smooth out the bumps in the road a little quicker and that is why we are here with you today.

More Than a Moment

Let's get back to 'the moment'. There really isn't just one moment. It is not like you flip a switch and all of a sudden one day you forget all the self-hate, the tantrums in front of the mirror because you don't feel comfortable in anything, the years you spent self-harming your thighs because you believed you were so fat and disgusting, all of that time built up to believing you are wrong and need to change in order to be right does not go away in a single moment. There are a number of moments that all add up to get you started and then there are many more moments on your journey that keep you going.

There is one moment though that set off a question in my mind, "Do I really have to live my life on a diet forever?" A few years ago, I began to read a book called *The Goddess Revolution* by Mel Wells. The cover was vibrant and the vibes that came across were all about girl power, which is something that lights me up (may explain how we are here together!). As I began to read I came to a section which said you don't have to live your life on a diet, "healthy eating plans" are basically a diet in disguise and food restricting of any kind is considered disordered eating. Oh, and you can be happy and healthy and still eat what you want.

I closed the book. *Is she mad? If I could eat whatever I wanted I would live on pasta, cheese, and chocolate, but I would be the size of a house! Restricting is not bad. If you want to be skinny you can't eat whatever you want!* I did not touch the book again for over a year, but that was the moment that set off a million questions in my mind, "Is she right? Do I really have to live my life on a diet, constantly worrying about what I am eating? Could I possibly be happy at a bigger size?" and although I was in complete denial, it's an important moment to have.

At this point in my life I was a single mother to three young children. My twins were around two and going through testing as they were behind in speech and communication as well as other areas too. My mental wellbeing was rocky, but I painted that smile on and kept my guard up. I was also training to be a fitness instructor and creating my brand BootyCamp. Although I was always about empowering women; at this time I was much more in the mindset of skinny = happy/healthy/beautiful. I was never happy with my results, there was never a moment of celebrated success, it was a constant battle of "I need to be better and do better."

After having the twins just fourteen months after my first born and only being twenty-one years young, I felt so much pressure to get back to my 'pre-baby body' that it took a hold of me. I tried diet after diet, some scarily low in calories, other seriously confusing, until I found one and stuck with it and although it was a "healthy living plan" it definitely aided my unhealthy relationship with food. I talk more about this in my book "Stretched: A mother's journey to love her 'flaws' & how you can too" so I will not go into full details of it all here.

The pressure I put on myself was immense and as I lost the weight the 'flaws' that pregnancy left on my body became even more visible. I had imagined my self-esteem would increase as the pounds dropped but it was in fact the opposite, the more I lost the more self-conscious I would feel about my imperfect body. Even as I was given compliments on my weight loss, words that I had longed to hear, I was feeling disgusted on the inside. *If they could see underneath these clothes, they would not be saying this to you right now.*

I felt like a complete imposter. The little demon was well and truly out in full force, filling my head with negative stories. It spurred my obsession with food and then my addiction to working out, which led me to train to become a fitness instructor. I went from being the girl who hated PE at school and all sports, to working out 6 times during one childfree weekend – yes this is a fact, it popped up on my Facebook Memories once and I could not believe it. *What? Why? How is that even possible?* When you are in that mindset you don't see the grip that the need to be loved, accepted, and seen as beautiful the way society's standards are set, has over you. You do not realise how much it takes over your own mental health.

This is Why Diets Do Not Work

You set a weight loss goal say fourteen pounds, you have an end destination say an awards evening, you put this pressure on yourself, pressure on yourself, pressure on yourself. Something inevitably challenges you in your personal and professional life, you turn to food and/or alcohol to give you some relief. Then you punish yourself for not sticking to your diet. You put more pressure on yourself, more pressure on yourself, more pressure on yourself. Another challenge pops up and the cycle goes round and round again.

This is called emotional eating; IT IS NOT A BAD THING! It is only seen as a bad thing because it is "off plan" or you are "cheating". Giving all these negative connotations to coping with life, that can be very difficult at times, is not good. Sometimes we turn to food for comfort, I repeat, it is not a bad thing. Sometimes you need a release, you need that comfort (there are a lot worse things you could be doing also!) and the more pressure you put on yourself to diet and lose weight the more you will turn to emotional eating.

Through this cycle, you don't hit your goal weight and when you get to your end destination, do you pat yourself on the back and say you gave it a go? Telling yourself that you are still worthy of love and beauty, go have a fun night? No, you don't, this is not how your brain works. Out comes the little demon that sits on your shoulder and you carry it around with you all night telling you those negative stories, "She's looking at you thinking why is she wearing that, it makes her butt look huge... why did you even come tonight? You didn't stick to your diet, you do not deserve to be in this room when everyone else is so much prettier than you are... why don't you just go home, you do not belong here!" I know this because this was me, a moment from my journey.

You beat yourself up, you feel like a failure, you feel like you have let yourself down. When in reality it is not you who has failed, it is the diet that has failed you. Look at it this way, the diet industry is worth billions of dollars, if diets worked we wouldn't need that industry anymore, everyone would be a 'healthy weight' no one would fail a diet and need to jump on the band wagon again. We have all been sucked into a world where being slim is idolised, put up on a pedestal, and has become the unattainable goal that everyone is desperate to reach.

The diet industry puts out the message across their adverts that when the subject speaking is heavier, they are sad, lonely, bored, self-conscious, etc, etc. all negative feelings and emotions. Then when the subject in question has lost weight, through their plan or weight loss aids, they are happier, more social, more confident. Like losing weight will answer all your problems.

I know from first-hand experience that this is not the case. If you have read *Stretched,* my first book, you will know the full story, but after I had lost three stone, I fully expected to have all those feels. I thought all my worries would just wash away. Did they? Some did yes, but then a whole load of other insecurities popped up and I treated myself even worse than I did before.

My 'flaws' as I saw them stopped me from being the happy, social, confident person that was on the TV ad or social media post. I had changed physically yes, but I had not changed emotionally, mentally, soulfully. I still did not believe that I was worthy of love, beauty, or happiness because I did not look exactly like all the "fitsporation" did. I had a mum tum and a very saggy one at that, the loose skin on my stomach haunted me with clothes off and when I was dressed and people would compliment my weight loss I felt like a huge imposter. *If only they knew the truth. If they could see me with my clothes off, they would be horrified, utterly disgusted. I know I look different to everyone else; I cannot let this be my reality, I need to work harder.*

Every personal trainer I knew that I asked for advice told me the same thing "It's just the stubborn fat, eat cleaner and train harder it's the last bit to burn." Of course these were all men, so why on earth I listened to them in the first place is beyond me, yeah I'm sure they are trained to a high ability but if you have never given birth how can you get a grip on the full extent it does to your body?

I battled with it for years and this is why I became addicted to exercise, I went to the gym six times in one weekend because I wanted to run away from the person I was and so desperately wanted to come out with someone else's body. I was in such a mentally focused zone that I was using fitness, something that should be a positive, to physically torture myself. I was so obsessed to battle this 'flaw' that I was completely blind-sided. In reality it is not going away, it never will naturally, it would disappear with surgery of course, though thankfully before I got to that level of desperation I found the path of self-acceptance to then find full true self-love and food freedom.

So how could we look at this in a different way, you are going to always have these end destinations, awards evenings, parties, weddings, holidays, New Years, etc. when all the diet ads turn to you and prey on your insecurities, how could we stop this pressurised restrictive emotional eating cycle? Here is how we could look at it...

Our end destination: awards evening
Our goal: to have fun and be present

On the lead up to the awards evening we find a fabulous dress that fits comfortably, no matter what size, we love it, it makes us feel fabulous. We wear said dress along with our chosen fabulous look for our make-up and hair, we get to the venue, we have a drink cocktail/mocktail whatever floats your boat (I'll have a pornstar martini please). You look around the room at all the other fabulous people who surround you, you smile, you breath in the love and you breath out the self-hate, you repeat "I am beautiful and surrounded by beauty, there is room for everyone to flourish." You kick that little demon to the curb, you compliment other people, you accept compliments, you smile, you dance, you have fun and you be present in the moment.

Now, I know this is easier said than done, but I promise you that taking away that pressure to lose weight for an event gives you so much more room to breathe, to live fully and to experience. Throughout this book you will find tools and techniques that I have used and still use on my self-love journey, step into my power, and flourish. There are also going to be other resources for you to use through audio and video on www.selflovedetox.com/lovethybody to help you on your journey. If man can go to the moon, you can learn to love the skin you are in.

Hello, I'm Struggling

As a mother, I spend the majority of my life running around after mini people who have all my sass, stubbornness and will power, it's tiring. Plus, all the other duties that come with being a mother and running a business on top, so I know just how hard it is to find the time to look after myself as well as everyone else. However, I have learnt the hard way what happens when I don't take care of myself.

Last year when I wrote *Stretched* I opened a can of worms, it was not until I was sitting down and rereading my first draft that I really realised how dieting, obsessive weight loss and being addicted to exercising wasn't just something normal that we all go through. It was not until then that I realised it was a massive strain on my own mental health. As I'm sure most of you all do to, I came to realise that I was spending far too much time with a mask on, putting on my happy face and brushing my real struggles and emotions under the carpet.

Each knock to my mind would be like the shake of a coke can, until it got too much, and the coke can exploded aka I lost my shit. *Is there a better way to phrase that?! Probably, but is it an accurate description? Yes, yes, it is.*

For as long as I can remember I have grown up believing that mental health just covered more extreme illnesses like depression, bipolar, PTSD, etc. I really did not know much about mental health; it was not a topic that was widely talked about until recently. Now I know much more about mental wellbeing and my knowledge has widened to knowing more conditions that come under the mental health umbrella. I look back at my life and realise how shaky my mental health has been over the years.

Although I'm a very positive person on the outside, I overthink everything, I struggle behind closed doors with some issues that people would be shocked at. Like I hate talking on the phone, but I can jump on a Zoom call, a Facebook Live or Instagram stories no problem. I have never been able to truly understand it until I learnt more about anxiety. This is all a new journey for me, and it is genuinely all coming out after choosing to write my story where I was aiming to empower women with my growth in confidence.

In October 2019 after various attempts over many weeks at making an appointment with the doctors, I was sitting in the surgery waiting room absolutely terrified. Every time the *bing bong* went off and called a patient in, my throat tightened and all the air supply was cut off from my brain for a few seconds and as a different name was called I released in relief, only to remember that my name would be coming at some point.

As I was sitting there twiddling my thumbs wondering what on earth I was going to say, an email popped up on my phone. Normally the internet is so terrible in the Doctors that you can never get anything to load, but this did. The email was from BBC Radio Oxford, I had been on a few times previously to share my mission and the book. Here is what the message said...

Hi Ana,

I hope this finds you well.

I'm getting in touch because I wondered if you might be free to come into our studios and do an interview at 10am on either the 20th, 21st or 22nd of November (next Wednesday – Friday).

I produce the Kat Orman show on BBC Radio Oxford and am trying to get together a whole week where we talk to inspirational local women about what they do and how they've reached the point where they are, as well as what advice they would give to young girls who aspire to be like them.

Sophie Law recommended you as someone who would be perfect to chat to about this – and if live at 10am isn't an option, we could also do a pre-recorded interview at 1pm most days.

Do let me know what will work best for you
– fingers crossed we can work something out!
Best wishes,
Lottie

I laughed under my breath, like a scoff almost, *oh the irony, here I am waiting to admit that I need help, that I'm not coping well, I'm not even sure how I'm feeling and they want me to talk as an inspirational woman? I don't feel very inspirational right now.* I sat and thought about it and then the doctor popped her head round the corner, and she said it "Ms Bonasera?" *Here we go.*

I didn't really know what to say, other than "I'm struggling" and to be honest I didn't say much the whole 8 minutes I was in the room, she asked me what were my other symptoms, *symptoms?! I don't have a clue, what am I supposed to be looking for?!* Although I was at a bit of a loss, she did give some good suggestions for some self-help sites and then told me that I had to self-refer to our local mental health assessment team. I had to phone them up!!! However, I found a way round it (kinda) you could fill in a form and request a call back, yeah slightly cheating but I did speak to them when they called me.

When they rang the first time it was nothing heavy, just basically booking me in for a thirty-minute telephone assessment and explaining how it would work. I had to fill in a questionnaire online first so that they could understand where I was at.

I booked in for my telephone consultation and here

comes some more sweet juicy irony for you. It was the afternoon of the day I had agreed to go on the radio to talk as an 'inspirational woman'. *Oh, sweet Jesus, Mary mother of God. What have I done?! What am I doing?! Can you really be inspirational while you're going through all of this?* I cried, I cried a lot during this time, I mean who am I kidding I am always overly emotional and crying at something, but this was a deep gut-wrenching cry that ached all over. I was sitting in the car pulled over on the side of the road contemplating what on earth was I doing with my life.

I decided that the only way I was going to get through this was to be totally honest and open. At this moment in time I was really suffering and in a much darker place, the sleepless nights from a baby is hard enough but add in the sleep deprivation from autistic twins and it is soul destroying and it literally puts all of your worries on steroids. Instead of seeing a mouse, you are seeing a big beefy rat with pulsating biceps. It made me over think everything, *she's thinking this about me, what have I done wrong, why aren't I included, they're talking about me aren't they?* My eyes were tired, and my brain was buzzing.

I went on the radio and I told the truth about where I was when I received the email and how I was struggling and the presenter of the show, Kat, was so lovely and encouraging it made me feel a little better.

I unfortunately did not get offered any help through the self-referral service, in fact I had a rather negative experience with it, and it left me feeling worse and helpless. We really do need to up our game when it comes to mental health services but there are charity lines that are there to talk to you, which I'll drop below, but even though I had a bad experience I still want you to try because everyone is different, you, me, and the other people on the end of the phone.

For myself, this did tip me over the edge, the coming days I had an all-time low and I did reach out to a text line just to talk and afterwards I began to feel stronger and found other ways that helped me cope. I really recommend audio books, they can be such a saving grace, I found Gabby Bernstein and had her playing continuously for a few weeks when I was feeling down, when I was doing the dishes, sorting the laundry, etc. I really recommend these books and you can find all resources and recommendations at:

www.selflovedetox.com/lovethybody

Pandas UK open 7 days a week open 9am-7pm
0808 196 776 free from UK landlines

Mind mental health charity open 5 days a week 9am-6pm
Call 0300 123 3393
Or text 86463

Crisis text line 24/7
85258

Samaritans charity 24/7
116 123

Sharing my story, opened up my mind to see my struggles in full colour for the first time, it allowed me to feel again. It was overwhelming with all of the other factors that I had going on in my life at the time but a year on I can look back now and feel so much stronger for having gone through it. It was actually therapeutic, and I really recommend doing it, if you're considering it let us know we are bringing together women in collaboration books to share their own stories and heal their wounds.

Self-love is not all bubble baths and blow dries; it is about facing your true self on your best days and more importantly on your worst days and finding the strength to keep going and step into your power.

As I was sitting in the doctors surgery and received that email, I laughed and I doubted myself, but everything happens for a reason, from that I was then asked to record a video for the BBC News website about my journey. I truly believe that putting yourself out there, making yourself vulnerable, and sharing your struggles speaks to those who have been through similar moments themselves. It shows that we are all human and that we are not alone in facing these hard times. I hope that if you need a nudge to get some help or a reminder that you are not the only one going through this that this is your nudge. You've got this!

To Judge or to be Judged

There are two directions that we are going to look at this from and I am going to give you different ways to deal with these directions. When it comes to comparing it is actually something that is naturally programmed into us, so if you come from the side of being the one to judge another, don't panic you are not a bad person. It is actually a natural programme that has been set in stone since the stone ages. We used this comparison technique to decide whether we were going to live or die, could we take on this Sabre Tooth Tiger or were we going to be his dinner? In the modern-day world, it pops in in much more of a negative tone. Do you ever catch yourself thinking "What on earth is she wearing?" "Why has she done that with her hair?" "What does she look like?" I am guilty of doing it and unless you are the Dalai Lama then you would be lying if you said you didn't.

We use comparison to judge others for what they are doing, what they are wearing, how they live, etc. It is those instant reactions that compare but it is the thought that comes second that is the judgement and the thought that comes third that makes or breaks you.

Like I said before, don't beat yourself up if you find that you are comparing yourself to or beginning to judge one of your sisters from another mister, if you are noticing that you are taking part in this negative reaction then that is an amazing starting point.

Noticing that you are having these thoughts of comparison or moving on to judgement is the first step, once you notice these thoughts and begin to catch them in the moment then you can take the time to step back and flip the script.

Now think why you are having this negative judgement. Is it because this is something you wished you were brave enough to do? Could it be because it is abnormal to your reality, if it is not hurting you then does it matter? Perhaps you are just joining in with the crowd, trying to fit in? There are many different reasons, but these I normally find are the top ones.

Next, flip the script, change your judgemental thought into a positive one. It might not be something you like or would do but that is what's beautiful about being human; we are all individual and unique, other people are free to do whatever they like and want and so are you.

Why not use the phrase "you do you girl" as an affirmation? Whenever you have a judgemental thought just whip out a "you do you girl" with a hair flip and some sass! I love this phrase, I do think it can be taken in a bitchy, sarcastic tone, but it's not about that at all, it's about showing that we can celebrate diversity all around us. We might not like the same things, dress the same way, watch the same films, like the same food, but there is room for everyone and everything that they like in this big scary world. It is not about everyone being the same, it is not about having everything in common, let's celebrate differences across the board, across genders, races, bodies, classes, etc. "You do you girl".

What happens when it is the other way round though? What about when you are the one who is feeling the eyes of a thousand people on you as you walk down the street? What if you are the one who feels like the whole world is judging you for what you look like, the choices you make or how you live?

When that feeling of self-consciousness washes over us that little demon sat on our shoulder pipes up and begins to fill our minds with negative stories "She thinks you are too fat to wear this… she thinks you look a mess today… she thinks you are trying too hard… she's thinking what on earth are you even doing here?" You create this narrative; do you notice how it is always negative? It's never "I bet she's thinking I look pretty good today… I bet she's wondering where my dress is from… I bet she's too shy to come and talk to me because I'm a nice person" nope, it's never the positive side of the story that we tell ourselves in our minds.

It is the constant dark thoughts that the little demon on our shoulder wants us to believe. It is easier for us to put ourselves down than to believe that someone could possibly be giving us a compliment. This comes a lot down to our own insecurities, how secure we are, or not, within ourselves.

I never ever used to leave the house without makeup on. In fact, I would put my "face on" one day, go to bed that night and wake up with a full face of makeup still on and do the school run again. No joke, I used to sleep in my make up, I know, I know, if you don't take your make up off for bed you add seven years to your skin. I have learnt that the hard way (haha just kidding these wrinkles are the product of autistic twins that do not know the difference between night and day and keep me up all night) but I would only sleep in the makeup because I wouldn't have time to do it the next morning and there was no way I'd leave the house with a bare face. Any time I did leave the house baring all (just my face) people would stop me and say "Are you okay? You look ill!" nope that's just my natural pale skin, thank you for pointing it out and making me feel even more self-conscious about not wearing makeup. It was definitely part of my need to keep up this facade that I was not struggling, that made me keep painting my happy face on.

But those feelings when the hairs on the back of our neck stand up and we assume it's because there are eyes burning into the back of our head, thinking the most evilest thoughts about ourselves that we can think of, those feelings usually are not valid.

It is time for us to flip the script from negative to

positive, it is time to hush that little demon on your shoulder and kick him to the curb, bye bitch bye! Something I need to make you aware of to help you when you're stuck in the anxious feeling that everyone is judging you, these people could be random people on the street as you pass them by or it could be people you see day to day, whoever it is it's highly unlikely you're going to ever know what they are thinking internally. So why choose to torture yourself when this is the story you are constantly telling yourself.

Flip the script, but how do we do it?

- Right now I want you to write out a list of three to five things you love about yourself, it does not have to be anything physical, it can be a personality trait and of course it can be a mixture too, for example I am passionate about helping others. I am a good listener. I love my eyes. Write these on a piece of paper that you can keep near you at all times or on the note's app of your phone.
- When you catch the little demon sneaking in with those negative thoughts, take a big deep breath, in through the nose and out through the mouth.
- Rewrite the script! Take out your list and rewrite the story, instead of "that looks hideous on her" you could flip it to "I really love her quirky taste, I wish I could be more confident with her style".

You are writing your story, make it a good one.

Aren't You Tired Yet?

I spent so long running away from who I am, trying to be like someone else. Trying to be like the picture-perfect people we see on our screens, on the TV, in films, on billboards, in the clothes we want to buy, on social media, walking down the street. We look at all those moments of peoples' life and envy them. We assume that they have got their shit together, that they are full to the brim with confidence and have everything they want.

I was running and running, constantly avoiding mirrors, trying to be someone I was not, denying myself of what I loved, physically and emotionally changing myself in hope that one day I would be like them. *Aren't you tired yet? You might as well give up; you will never be like them!* I never will be like them, that was maybe the best lesson I could have ever learnt and the greatest advice I could ever give.

You will never be like them. You can only be like you. It doesn't matter how far you run, until you stop, until you listen to what you truly need, until you realise your worth just as you are, you will always be tired. Emotionally drained from pretending to be something you are not.

Like pretending that you like 98% dark chocolate – unless you are the devil or a complete psycho who the hell eats darker than dark chocolate for fun, more like torture. I love Cadburys Dairy Milk and I will no longer deprive myself of eating what I love because at the end of the day, I would rather eat chocolate and be the size I am than be super skinny and still be bloody miserable.

Aren't you tired yet? You might as well give up; you will never be like them. All those picture-perfect moments that you see are only one sided, you do not know how they feel behind the screen, behind the brave front they put on. We have no idea what goes on in other people's heads, they could quite easily be just as unhappy about their body as you are. I'm sure they feel immense pressure and even though they look perfect to you, they will be constantly comparing themselves to someone else with the 'ideal body' and the chain continues, *aren't they tired yet?!* Probably, they probably are exhausted, emotionally drained from people saying "Oh I wish I had your body... you're so lucky I'd kill to look like you... I would love your confidence" and underneath the smile, the nod and the polite "thank you's" she could be aching inside. Mentally torturing herself for eating a 'cheat' meal at the weekend, for not exercising that morning or going out and having a few drinks with her friends and not 'sticking to plan'.

I know those feelings all too well, my mental health

was stretched so far that I could not see how amazing I looked. I punished myself for still having all of these 'flaws' that come with life and having a baby, my skin was not perfectly smooth, and I did not have toned abs. Even though I actually had a pretty good start on my abs, but because underneath the waistband to my gym leggings was holding in my loose skin from having twins, for me it was never enough.

All of this crazy shit doesn't just go on in your head, we have all been programmed to believe that unless we look a certain way we need to run away from who we are and run towards the impossible picture perfect body. Aren't you tired yet of running? Aren't you tired of punishing yourself for not looking picture perfect? Aren't you tired of putting yourself down for having fun with your friends? Aren't you tired of feeling inferior to those who are smaller, curvier, fitter, happier etc. than you?

You will never be like them and that is the beauty of the world. We are a diverse nation and that is what we should celebrate. Diversity is a beautiful thing, it makes us interesting and I know that you and I are so much more interesting than what we did (or didn't) eat for lunch or what number is in the back of our jeans. I am not running away anymore, and I want you to stop running, to hold my hand and together we can walk towards self-love.

Fraud from the Inside Out

"You look amazing" has a completely different meaning to "you are amazing" can you see the difference? We live in a world obsessed about looks, right, wrong, good, bad, happy, sad, ugly, beautiful, fat, thin, short, tall, etc. I used to long for people to comment on my weight loss after I had my twins and I was obsessed with trying to get my 'pre baby body back' I was desperate for people to say "You look good for just having twins!"

I tried many a diet after I had the boys, after one which I called the 'silver sachet diet' (basically mixing powder with water and calling it food) I lost a scary ten pounds in two weeks. Yet I still was not happy with how I looked, I had not hit a one stone loss (fourteen pounds), I emotionally abused myself and repeatedly told myself it was not good enough.

This diet was in preparation for an awards ceremony for my dad's business. I felt so uncomfortable on the night, I was so conscious that the dress I had ordered, in a size smaller than I really needed, did not fit and was pinching me under my armpits. I did hear those words I was longing to hear though "You look good for just having twins!" I thanked them being polite, but I felt like a complete fraud, I felt like they were just saying it to be kind.

I have always struggled to take compliments, especially when it was about my appearance. It makes me go all cringey and act like a silly sausage (okay not so cute might delete that later…) even now with how I look or around success with my business I still get super awkward and even though I am excited and happy I am also feeling on edge. Why? Why do I get like this? And if it is something you relate to why do we get like this? It has nothing to do with what they are saying and everything to do with our own beliefs.

How do you see yourself? Do you see yourself? A kind person, a beautiful woman, a good mother/wife/ friend? Or are you normally calling yourself stupid for losing the keys again, a failure for not keeping on top of the housework and a bad mother/wife/friend because you could do more? I am definitely guilty of speaking to myself like the latter!!

Even though I am a positive person and I am the first person to pick up everyone else and tell them they are amazing, I am so critical on myself. Yes, it is human nature but no this does not make it okay! We must change this; how much longer can we continue putting ourselves down before it seeps into our everyday life and affects those around us? This negative self-talk was the reason I started my brand Self-love Detox back in January 2019, it's how I came to meet Serena and

Laura and do all of the other amazing body positive and mental health activist things I have done over the last couple of years.

In December 2018 with Christmas looming and all the end of year school meetings, plays, coffee mornings etc. I was extremely stressed; I was losing my shit on the regular and it wasn't even my time of the month! (Yes, it is okay to admit if periods make you extra on edge). I had been through such a positive experience with my body, felt so confident and kicked that demon to the curb, I could not work out why I was going through this?

Then I listened to the voice inside my head, the little demon was back, and he had found new 'flaws' to feed off of. "You are so stupid, you forget everything. You're a bad mum everyone is judging you." Calling myself stupid and a bad mother was and is something I still call myself, that little demon and the comparison with the picture perfect and Pinterest mothers puts untold amounts of pressure on us. We must put an end to this.

When I realised this back at the end of 2018 that is when I decided to create the Self-love Detox girl power support group to hold myself accountable on my own journey by empowering other women to go on theirs. Although this is still a demon I battle with, I find different tools that help me to put them at bay.

Recently the whole "bad mother" card has been played a lot, with lockdown, home schooling, working from home and trying to keep the house from falling apart the mum guilt has been real. My parents, Jordan, friends and even Nathaniel all correct me and tell me I am a good mum, but I find that such a massive jump from the "bad mum" title I have given myself.

When I am doing affirmation work with ladies I understand that loving yourself is not an over-night success and we can't just go from "I hate my body" to "I love my body" so we find an in between "I am learning to accept my body 'flaws' and all". Therefore, I decided I needed to find an in between good and bad mum title. I present to you Ana Louise Bonasera the "I'm trying my best mum" ta-dah! Fancy, huh? *Haha* okay it is a bit long and a bit of an odd one maybe, but I am constantly questioning myself, *am I doing the right thing?* But reality is, there is no right or wrong in this job of parenthood, there is no manual, there is no guidebook, no two families are the same, everything is different for every single mother.

There is no one right way, there are many different routes to take which can lead to the same outcome, therefore all we can do is what feels right for our family at that time. Sure, we will make mistakes, okay, we will take a longer route sometimes, but we can always find our way in the end. I am a "doing my best" mum, feel free to join our club! Affirmations are powerful and can really impact positively on you for your mental wellbeing, and your self-talk about body confidence, we are going to dig deep on this now, ready, set, go…

STEP ONE. WHY FAILING IS NOT YOUR FAULT...

It is Christmas or summer or any excuse for the diet industry to guilt trip us into starting a new weight loss programme. For example, lets say it is "Little black dress challenge: feel more confident at your Christmas party this festive season by losing X amount of weight and dropping X amount of dress sizes." You buy a motivational dress that's two sizes too small, you starve, starve, starve, squeeze in a bit of exercise between work, school plays and Christmas parties – squeeze into a dress that's still at least a size too small "you look really great" feels good, that hard work was really worth it BINGE BINGE BINGE *three days after Christmas* crying on the floor in your pjs with chocolate wrappers all around you* "I'm a big fat mess." Then comes new year "New Year, New me. This time it is going to be different, I will not end up back here next year" fast forward to December 31st 2020 to you crying on the floor surrounded by chocolate wrappers sobbing...

Hmm, something seems wrong here, am I right? How many times have you started the new year thinking that next year it is going to be different, you are going to lose X amount of weight and drop X amount of dress sizes and feel happy and confident. How many times have you ended the year feeling like a failure? Or even getting to the end of January and beating yourself up because you can't even stick to a diet for a month?

You might feel like a failure, but it is not you who has failed the diet, it is the diet that has failed you. For a long time, I believed that losing a stone and a half was going to bring me pure happiness and true confidence and be the answer to all my problems. When I fell pregnant with my twins and my eldest was just nine months old, I felt like I had failed myself and it feels horrible to say but I did not have my 'pre-baby body' back yet. I felt cheated in a way. This mentality took over my whole pregnancy and although I enjoyed being pregnant; I was wishing it away; I was desperate to lose weight. When the twins came early, I actually saw it as a positive because I could start my diet sooner!! How sad and awful does that sound?!

I literally counted down the days until I could start a diet at six weeks postpartum, I took drastic measures to take part in this diet where I literally starved myself and when I lost ten pounds within two weeks it still wasn't enough. That is an unhealthy amount of weight, to lose in that time frame but to me it was not a stone, it was not enough. It was not enough at ten pounds and it was not enough when I found an eating plan that helped me lose double my goal weight, almost three stone in six months – it was never going to be enough. But why? Why did I feel like a failure even though I had hit my goal? Why wasn't it enough? Because no matter how much I changed myself on the outside it was never going to change how I felt on the inside and that is where I was going wrong.

STEP TWO. ESTABLISHING OUR LIMITING BELIEFS

What do you believe about your body? Do you believe it is wrong or right? Do you believe it is beautiful or ugly? Do you believe it is happy or sad? Do you believe it is fat or thin? Do you believe it is disgusting or worthy? Do you believe it deserves to be loved or hated? Do you believe it deserves to feel confident or self-conscious? What do you believe about your body? I want you to pause right now and spend some time really thinking what you believe about your body.

After I had lost all that weight I felt even more self-conscious than ever because even though I was finally getting those compliments that I had been craving "You look amazing for having had twins" and I would nod my head and give a half smile, inside I would be emotionally torturing myself. *They are only saying that, no one really believes it and anyway if they saw you with your clothes off they'd be running for the hills.* I genuinely believed that the 'flaws' that postpartum had left on me; including my cellulite, stretch marks and 'mum tum' which was my biggest heart ache made me undeserving. I had all this loose skin that fell from my stomach, stretched, empty, and sagging even more now from losing weight. I hit a new low. I wrote an example of how I would talk to my body if I was doing this exercise right now…

I believe that my body is ugly and disgusting, I believe that I should be ashamed of it and cover it up,

I believe that I do not deserve to wear jeans at a bigger size, so I wear black leggings to hide away. I believe that no man will find me attractive so I will not date and if I do, I will push anyone away who tries to get close. I believe that I am unworthy of love. I believe that people talk about me wherever I go, I believe that people stare at me because of how awful I look. I believe that my body is wrong.

Now, I want you to pick someone you love dearly your child, partner, your best friend or loved one, think about how much you love them, care for them and how thankful you are for them.

Now read this statement again, swap "my body" to "you/r body" and imagine you are saying this to them.

I believe that your body is ugly and disgusting, I believe that you should be ashamed of it and cover it up. I believe that you do not deserve to wear jeans at a bigger size, so you should wear black leggings to hide away. I believe that no man will find you attractive so you should not date and if you do you will push anyone away who tries to get close. I believe that you are unworthy of love. I believe that people talk about you wherever you go, I believe that people stare at you because of how awful you look. I believe that your body is wrong.

How does that make you feel? Would you ever say that to your child or loved one? Would you ever even think it? No? Me neither! Then why do we treat ourselves this way? This is heart breaking to imagine, right? It fills me with tears just thinking about it. Our beliefs are the start of everything, in the next step we are going to work on rewriting our beliefs and learning how they are the beginning of building our confidence, well done for getting through that, this is not easy and it is not something you have to do right now, you can come back to it, but keep reading soak it up and take as much from it as you can.

Step Three. Rewriting your limiting beliefs

Perhaps you are sat there thinking "what the hell is she on about, how is this going to make me confident!?" But there is method in my madness, stick with me.

In step two we talked about your beliefs about your own body and how you would not talk to your own child, friend or loved one the way you talk to yourself. It is not your fault that you treat yourself so badly, this is something that is engraved into our brains from a very young age, taking in those around us who struggle to accept themselves, from the pressures of comparison to other people's perfect looking bodies and lives on social media and in the media. There are more forces telling us to judge ourselves, hate ourselves and change ourselves than there are telling you to love and accept yourself just as you are.

Enter me, Laura and Serena, this book, our online

communities, enter us, it is time for a Love Thy Body revolution ladies! Now let's learn a bit more about why exactly beliefs are such a huge factor to being confident.

Your beliefs turn into your thoughts, your thoughts turn into your feelings, your feelings turn into your actions and your actions turn into your results. We want the result to be confident and happy in our skin, loving who are we are exactly how we are, correct? But if your beliefs above are that you are anything but that, then can you see where we are going wrong? Being aware of what your current beliefs are is so powerful, self-awareness can help us transition to a new positive chapter. It is time for some new beliefs, but how on earth do we do that? Years and years of repeating to ourselves how disgusting and unlovable we are to all of a sudden being comfortable just as we are? This is not about being an over-night success, this is not a quick scale win, you are not going to get that instant gratification of losing three pounds in a day because you've had a big wee, a poop and starved yourself. We want this to be something that we work on each and every day, you got me?

The simplest way to do this, without taking up time, energy or money but making a difference to how we see and feel about ourselves is affirmations! Now, if you have never heard of affirmations before they are just short sentences, a mantra, that are positive, empowering and something you repeat to yourself, every day, multiple times a day. We have a lot of rewiring to do in our brains, but positive affirmations will help us undo this.

How on earth do we come up with an affirmation?! Well great news, you have basically been using affirmations already, so you know exactly what to do, you have just been using negative ones all of your life. I'm going to help you with the phrasing, plus I'm going to share some of my favourites, I've even made pictures you can save and use as screen savers for your phone wahoo! You can find them at www. selflovedetox.com/lovethybody

To start with you always want to make them about the present tense, "I am sensational" if you are really struggling to believe that you are these positive describing words then you can use a phrase like "I am learning to know my worth" "Each day I wake up feeling happier just as I am" something along those lines. If you need help, reach out, share in the group, we can support one another.

There are so many different areas of our life, you can be confident in some and a total shaky mess in others, that is okay, you are not expected to be an A* pupil in all your subjects. I am a confident person, I can do a Facebook live no problem, Zoom call you got it, speak on stage with a head set and over 2000 attendees (okay shaky) but I smashed it. However, picking up the phone = my biggest nightmare. When I am on the phone I can do it fine, I can hold a conversation and switch the confidence up but the thought fills me with dread and you will very rarely find me chatting on the phone still to this day.

Being a mother, I take a lot on, four kids, two with special needs, life is hectic, I am completely unconfident in my mothering ability, I constantly question myself and call myself a bad mother. My family try and reassure me that I am a good mum, but it is such a big leap for me to go from thinking I'm a bad mum, to a good mum, I just don't believe it! Therefore, I decided to come up with my own in between, I am a "doing my best mum" this is my happy medium and every time the little demon comes out on my shoulder and starts telling me I'm a bad mum, I flip the script and bring in my rewritten belief "I am a doing my best mum" because in an upside down world that was already overwhelming doing our best is the only thing we can do. You can use this rewritten belief in other circumstances too, business, jobs, partner, friend, etc. give yourself a break, be kinder, be understanding, just like you would to your best friend.

We'll Meet Again...

I do not think there could be any better way to end this, a fitting theme for the year 2020, a year with so much fun and laughter planned, which was replaced with loneliness, despair and uncertainty. "We'll meet again... " my eighty-something little granny tells me over the phone again and again as she is locked away safe in her home. I know there is a lot of sadness from this year (2020), I was due to be married on June 13th, we had a diary full of workshops to be with you all and see your transformations blossom in front of our very own eyes and so much more. From March to August in an instant, a blur, a flash, the year has not gone as planned, yet life never does. You visualise and imagine how your life will transpire and sometimes life throws you a hurdle, a different path a very bumpy journey.

I really found this a tough thing to get my head around a few years after the twins were diagnosed with autism, yes a few years, I think I was so proactive in the beginning to get help that a few years down the line it really hit me how life would not be as it was pictured. I became angry at life, I felt like we had a massive injustice, I felt the weight of the world on my shoulders and I did not want to let go of this cloud of doom over my head. It is really hard to explain unless you're in it and yes although it sounds totally selfish, I honour those feelings.

I will not stand by and push my hurt, sadness, or anxiety to the bottom, I honour them, I sit with them, I feel them, I take them in, and I move past them. Do not let anyone else tell you that you should be grateful for what you have, just because you are feeling the feels does not mean that you are not grateful. No one has the right to tell you how to feel. The more we hide, the more we bottle up, the bigger the explosion on the other side, it is okay to let it out. So however you are feeling about 2020 I want you to know that your feelings are valid, you are valid, you deserve to take up space, to be seen, to be heard just as you are emotionally as well as physically. This is goodbye for now, but this is not the end, this is just the beginning of a beautiful friendship. We'll meet again.

With love & gratitude,

Ana Louise Bonasera

Ana Louise Bonasera, is a mother of four boys, including her autistic twins, and over the past few years she had battled her body image and mental health. She openly shares her struggles in her book "Stretched: A mother's journey to love her 'flaws' &

how you can too". In the book and online she shares how dieting and the pressures of society affected her emotionally and physically. She is now on a mission to empower women to honour their 'flaws' and rule their clothes with confidence.

To find out more about Ana and her girl power community Self Love Detox head to

www.selflovedetox.com

SERENA NOVELLI

"We are all deserving of feeling sexually empowered no matter our race, colour, size, sexual preferences, or religion."

Unleash the Diva

When you start to work on your self-love it is imperative that you ensure that you are working on all aspects of your life, and for me sexual empowerment is a key element in this. Before I delve in a little deeper, pun intended, and share some of the strategies I have learned over time, working both on my own sexual desires and alongside my clients with their deepest desires. I really want to reiterate that ultimately the key element in truly finding who you are, and showing up as that confident version of you, comes from YOU taking the required action, to make those positive changes. We can support and guide you every step of the way but the real work comes from you and how ready you are to step up into your highest power and allow that inner diva to come out to play.

I absolutely love the work I do. How many women get to say that they get paid to explore their own body, play with toys, and learn daily about that old taboo subject of sex for a living right? It is funny though because if someone had told me in my early twenties that this would be exactly what I was doing I would have thought them crazy. You see everybody has a journey, a story to tell, and well mine was one of self-hatred, severe body dysmorphia, and sex, well sex scared the shit out of me.

You see those thoughts you have inside your head, you know the ones, the ones that tell you that you are not good enough, pretty enough, or worthy enough, well they have some explaining to do let me tell you. My head was full of little mind monkeys and there was no way I was going to be able to be a goddess in the bedroom with all that chatter going on. You see what you think effects how you feel and how you feel effects how you live your daily life, and if you are thinking and feeling as though you are not worthy or even close to being a sex goddess well then your sex life will mirror those thoughts.

Throughout my chapter in this book I am going to be open and honest and share my own sexual empowerment journey with you. I am also going to share a few of the techniques and tools myself and my clients use when working on sexual awakening journeys. I also want you to know that we are all very different, our journeys will differ, our background, support system, and how we live our life will all have different factors. Yet we are all absolutely deserving of feeling sexually empowered no matter our race, colour, size, sexual preferences, or religion. In fact, nothing should stop you from feeling sexually empowered.

You must also know that you have the right to say 'no' and should not feel guilty, pressured, or forced when it comes to sex. Love making whether that is with a man, woman or with multiple lovers should always be consensual. Sex is about feeling good and pleasured and you are deserving of the most amazing sex and mind-blowing orgasms just as much as the next person is. It is imperative that you understand this right from the start.

Now, let us go unleash that inner diva from within.

The Female Body

As women with all that social media and the beauty standards throw our way it is so easy to get lost in a world of comparison. We see images of the "Ideal" body wherever we go, on TV, on our social media, on billboards, in magazines, and even the mannequins in shops can portray an image of the ideal body shape.

Women's bodies have become overly sexualised over time. We have been conditioned to think we have to look and feel a certain way and if we do not well there is something wrong with us. We put pressure on ourselves to conform, we use the very things that these images have been designed for in an attempt to fit in. We turn to diet pills, makeup, in trend clothes, lip fillers, the lot, and then we are criticised and labelled for doing so. Now I am not saying that using these products or wanting to feel a certain way is wrong, what I am saying is if we can look at our bodies for what they are, we could then make informed decisions on the product/services we use to aid our wellbeing, without the fear of comparison.

The female body is a powerful, magical vessel you just need to think of what it goes through during puberty, childbirth, and even menopause to realise this. We are born with everything we need in order to reproduce and ensure the existence of the human race. Our bodies instinctively know what is needed to house and keep our unborn child safe and warm as it grows and gets ready to embrace its first ray of light. Our cervix opens to a huge ten centimetres, around the size of a bagel, to allow a safe entrance as our newborn makes his/her way into our world. Our other organs make space during pregnancy to ensure that there is room for our womb to grow and do its job. Our bodies are truly magical indeed.

So, if our body knows what to do during childbirth it is safe to say it will also know how and what to do during sex, right? So why do we find it so difficult to let go and enjoy such a natural part of our existence? Why is sex and procreation so taboo? And why do we find it so uncomfortable to talk about despite it being one of the most natural biological behaviours?

Growing up, there were never really any conversations around sex in my home, even though my parents were not overly religious or afraid to put their own viewpoints out there, it just was not talked about. Sex education in school was a thirty-minute video that showed if you had sex you would fall pregnant and to be honest it completely scared the shit out of me. Then there was Sunday school which had me believing that to make babies you had to be in wedlock.

Even though society over sexualises the female

body to sell its products, it is also quick to label women when they show up as confident in the bedroom or a confident version of themselves. Slut, whore, easy, man eater are all words I most certainly heard growing up.

I fell pregnant with my son at just eighteen years old, I wasn't married at the time and I was worried of what people would think. I had been dating Adriano since I was sixteen years old, we are still together to this day and now have five wonderful children together. The sex between us at the time was awkward, I had not really had any experience when it came to the bedroom department. The only previous experience I did have hadn't been consensual, so I had no real idea what to do, how to act, or what to expect.

For a long time, I suffered with Body Dysmorphia and was really insecure, so I used plain baggy clothes and clowned around to try to hide my insecurities. Even with my lack of sexual experience or knowledge, my peers would spread rumours about me. I had apparently slept with at least three different boys in school before I had even lost my virginity. After having my son, I had grown women pass judgements on me. If I had a pound for every time someone said one-night stand baby, or single mum I would be rich.

By the time I was ready to get married my son was five years old. I remember the Vicar coming to my home to meet with us to start making the arrangements, and I remember the fear of being judged so I removed all existence of my son from the house before the visit. All that is apart from his action-man battery-powered motor bike. As the vicar entered my home and walked past the bike he commented "nice bike", and in my panic of thinking I would not be allowed to get married in church I replied back "yes that's how Adriano gets to work". I was so used to being judged by others that I had assumed he would be the same and I was already fearing the worst. Crazy right that I was letting other people's thoughts and opinions affect my own life.

As well as the taboos that surrounded me when it came to sex, I was also battling with my mental health. As my friends started to develop in school, I still had not. I would hear my peers talking about boyfriends, kissing, and exploring and I just did not think I was pretty enough, and no way was I going to let a boy anywhere near my boobs so I could be ridiculed. My body was not doing the same things as the other girls in my class, I was not growing and developing in the same way that they were.

I met a boy at age sixteen who was not good for me at all, but somehow, he had managed to convince my parents he was a saint. He suffered with jealousy and had a fierce temper, he liked a drink and I feared him. I kept my fears to myself though and hid them from those around me.

My first sexual experience was with him and was forced and not consensual at all. It was an unpleasant experience for me, I felt dirty, scared, and I had this horrible feeling in the pit of my stomach every time he touched me. I never reached out to anyone, I carried on acting as if everything was normal around my parents and when I was with him I just tried to block it out of my mind as though it had never happened.

I would never wish this on anyone, not even my worst enemy, and I hope to god that my children never feel this way, that they know they can speak to me no matter what.

AGAIN, the fear of judgement held me back, I had been raped and instead of seeking help I hid the experience and locked away the key. This experience left me feeling undeserving of love, it left me with emotional scars, and other than my husband I have never told anyone about this experience. So here I am sharing my soul with you, why? Because I want you to know that no matter your past sexual experiences you are so deserving of experiencing true pleasure in all areas of life.

ACTIVITY ONE

Letting go of fear of judgement.

When we live in a place of fear of judgement or comparison it is difficult to be able to move forward and enjoy the things we truly want in life. This activity is one that will help you to determine whether your preserved judgements are indeed fact or fiction.

Why is this important? Well remember those mind monkeys I mentioned earlier, they are continually bombarding us with mind chatter and our mind chatter comes from those preconceptions that we have built up about ourselves over time. Now you may have done this activity or something similar before whilst working on your self-love journey. This time I want you to work solely on your pre-conceptions about sex and how you should be treated in the bedroom.

Take around thirty minutes to work on this activity, do not rush it.

In your journal or notebook have a page marked fact and a page marked fiction and start to really think about what is holding you back when you are wanting to get your freak on. Do not be afraid to dive in deep (there she goes again with the puns) and really ask yourself "is this a fact or is it fiction?" Start to think about why you feel this way, what made you believe this? A fact is something that can be proved and cannot be changed. Fiction is something that can be perceived or interpreted differently by each person and so is something that can be changed.

For most of us we live in the mindset that everything is fact when in reality most things are actually changeable, it is only when you start to make these changes that you start to see a positive difference in what you experience.

For example:

Is this fact or fiction?

I can only have mind blowing sex after a few drinks.

Although this may be the case for some right now it is actually fiction because with the right work it is absolutely achievable to enjoy sex wherever and however you choose.

No cheating now, make sure you complete this task before continuing to read this book. Remember you are stepping up to empower yourself in all areas of self-love, so by skipping you are doing yourself an injustice.

God Gave Us Fingers.

So I have spent fifteen years talking sex, I can talk sex absolutely anywhere and with anyone, in a queue at the supermarket, on the train, you name the place and it is highly likely I have or I would chat sex there. I chat sex with complete strangers daily via social media. I attend ladies only parties where sex is the topic of the moment and I empower a team of women to go out there and do the same. I do this so that we can live our lives feeling confident, sexy and empowered, without fear of judgement. I have come to notice that when women do talk about sex, they tend to get a little rose cheeked especially when I mention self-pleasure and masturbation. They giggle as I pass the sex toys around, but it is also one of the subjects they are very observant of.

As I mentioned earlier our bodies instinctively know what to do when it comes to sex, and it is evident that us women love to feel good in the bedroom. However, the stigma of society and our own preserved conceptions of ourselves in any given moment, tend to hold us back from living out our deepest fantasies.

Sexual empowerment begins from within, it is not

something we can cosmetically change. It is about embracing your sexuality, owning your deepest desires, and devoting time to working on yourself so that you are fulfilling and enjoying a loving relationship with yourself first and foremost.

Exploring yourself sexually is key to a happier, healthier sex life, it means being able to continually seek out knowledge of your sexual preferences and desires.

Equally as important is gaining the knowledge of what experiences or characteristics you do not want your sex life to include. Knowing these will help you gain better more fulfilling sexual experiences with both your partner and alone.

This discovery should be fun and enjoyable, and it should not be dependent on anybody else. It is so important to discover and explore your sexuality and to do so without fear of judgement. Whilst exploring with a partner is great, it should not be your only method; you need the space to be able to explore what you like, and what you do not without any outside influences.

Exploring your sexuality on your own will also help you to learn just how beautiful your body really is, it will help you become more in tune with your bodies needs both emotionally and physically. It will help you to be in the moment, in the flow, in that feminine energy. Women who masturbate and explore their sexuality are more sexually confident in the bedroom, fact.

In my opinion self-exploration should be part of your daily self-care routine. As the more in tune that you are with your body and the way your body reacts when you feel good, the more sexually self-confident you will become.

Whilst masturbation should be a fun journey of self-discovery, I also want to take the opportunity to highlight the importance of masturbation and break some taboos. Did you know that 35% of heterosexual women are having fewer orgasms than anyone else? This absolutely must change. We should all be enjoying a healthy sex life whether it is with a partner or alone.

With men masturbation is a common subject and one that they are completely fine and happy to talk about, it is even widely joked about on our television screens, American Pie comes to mind here. Yet female masturbation is hardly ever talked about and many women feel embarrassed, guilty, or ashamed of themselves for enjoying masturbation, even though it is entirely healthy, natural, and should be encouraged.

Masturbation also releases all the best hormones including, dopamine, endorphins and oxytocin, also known as the love hormone. These are released through physical stimulation of your clitoris, vagina, cervix and breasts, so even if you do not reach the big O you will still feel totally amazing and certainly less stressed.

Masturbation also increases blood flow to both your brain and reproductive organs and can help to soothe headaches and period pains and can help you feel relaxed when you are feeling stressed, the sexual release along with the decrease in your cortisol levels also will help you to sleep better.

And now for my favourite of all the reasons; self-exploration helps you to have a better understanding of how your body works. When you understand what your body wants and needs, you strengthen your connection with your Mind Body Soul. You learn to love yourself fully and it helps to ensure you are showing up as the highest version of yourself daily.

As a teen and in my early twenties I hardly ever explored my body, I was ashamed and felt like it was something dirty, I later attributed this to my first sexual experience and my body dysmorphia. As a young girl I quite clearly remember exploring the sensations I felt when I discovered what was hiding within my knickers and it felt good. Then in my late teens things changed, and I would get highly embarrassed if a sex scene came on the tv and would have to make an excuse to leave the room.

I could not bear to be touched especially my breasts and I would not feel comfortable having sex with the lights on. Sex for me became an obligation something I did not really enjoy unless I had a few glasses of wine in me. It was not that my partner was not loving or doing a good job. It was me.

I was not happy with my appearance, my mind chatter was a constant bombardment of self-hatred, and loathing. I could not look in the mirror without seeing a part of me I wanted to change. It did not matter how much Adriano told me I was beautiful or how much he loved me, because I never believed him. I did not love myself so how could I believe that someone else loved me? The only times I really felt good in the skin I was in was when I was carrying our beautiful children.

I lived my life in a constant battle because I could feel the real Serena somewhere deep down inside of me, but I could not find how to let her out. It was not until my oldest daughter was about three and I noticed her using negative self-talk that I realised I had to put on my big girl pants and make some changes. What I did not realise was this would be in the form of sexual empowerment.

2005 saw me embark upon a journey I never thought I would, I decided to jump in with both feet and become an Ann Summers party organiser. What was I thinking, me the girl who could not even enjoy an intimate moment with the man she loved without criticizing her own performance was now going to be selling sex products. But the universe only puts what you can handle in front of you, right? That is also why you are currently holding this book (just saying). So big girl underpants it was and boy what a magical journey.

I very quickly came to realise that I was not alone, most of the women I met, even the ones that I had longed to look like or envied at some point in my life, were not happy either. They had their own body image issues and sexual struggles too. This was my light bulb moment, this was when I realised I had the power to take charge of my own thoughts and feelings, I would liken it to a spiritual awakening. I was at rock bottom, and my daughter saved me. It was time to live as the empowered version of me.

I was growing in confidence, earning money doing something I enjoyed. I was starting to realise that my body was exactly that – my body – and it deserved to be loved. I was changing the way I spoke to myself, taking chances and setting goals that I once held back from, and I was trying my best to enjoy my sexual experiences.

Adriano asked me once how I could sell sex toys when I had not even tried them myself, it's funny because I had not even thought about it. I went on trainings, learned all about the products and I sold toys. If somebody asked me what sensations it gave or how good a product it was, I went from feedback from past customers or what I had learned at my trainings. It never occurred to me to buy my own personal stash and test them out.

I did buy the underwear and was great at selling these, so I decided why not, Adriano and I got ourselves a few toys to explore with and we started to have fun experimenting. Sex started to become something I enjoyed, I started to relax into the moment, let my body embrace the sensations of my partner's touch and trust that he had my back, this was certainly a sexual awakening for me, and the more I explored with and without my partner the more in tune with my body I became.

Sexual empowerment is not only about having intercourse it is about discovering the parts of you that make you tick. A women's body has heightened sensitivities and sensations to touch, bites, licks and even sound and most women absolutely loved to be nurtured and teased before we head on over for the home run. And as I stated at the beginning of this chapter not all women are the same, so it is imperative that we explore our bodies to find out what we love.

Let Us Talk Clit Power

Did you know that the clitoris actually extends three inches into the vagina and that there are around 8000 nerve endings down there which is twice as many as in the penis, and it does not end there! This tiny erogenous zone spreads the feelings to 1500 nerve endings in your pelvis. We have been gifted an organ that is solely for pleasure and boy is it powerful.

For self-exploration why not start off with what god gave you, yep therefore this section is aptly called #godgaveusfingers put your fingers to the test. Do not forget to lube up to add to and heighten the sensation. You can also buy a variety of clit stimulating toys from mini bullets that give precise stimulation to rechargeable power houses that vibrate on a low frequency sending uncontrollable sensations through-out your body. Massage wands and even suction wands are also available to help you explore what feels great for you.

Not forgetting the g spot, your sweet spot here is located around two to three inches from the wall of your vagina. Using lube and a come here motion with your fingers will allow you to explore the pleasure and sensations within this area. You can also buy glass dildos, love eggs, jiggle balls, and vibrators of all shapes and sizes to explore with. Do not forget the inner and outer labia that are full of incredible nerve endings for endless pleasure. As you explore your body and learn what is right for you, you are breaking free and owning your power.

ACTIVITY TWO

Time to explore.

You may have dabbled a little before or you may be brand new when it comes to self-exploration it doesn't matter where you are starting as this is your own personal journey and one not to be compared to others. The key is to take physical action, to push yourself just outside of that comfort zone. It is imperative that you feel safe and comfortable and are having fun whilst doing this activity.

So, the first task will be to find time and a safe space each day where you can play. Remember this does not have to lead to full blown orgasms every time and it does not have to be in the same place every time either.

It could be a morning shower with a little shower head fun. Maybe it is while you are applying your favourite body lotion and you watch how your body reacts to each touch. It could be reading your favourite erotic fiction. Perhaps a little bedroom fun with your favourite toy. Or maybe the practice of edging – the act of leading yourself to the point of orgasm but stopping just before you do, then repeatedly doing this until you reach the point of no return. Experimenting with pressure and testing out different ways to touch yourself.

You could try sensory deprivation; can you deny yourself touch whilst listening to a favourite erotic podcast or audible. Try out different lubricants and heat sensations. Explore places you have not tried with your partner yet. Use your fingers internally as you treat your clit to some good vibrations, tighten and relax your vagina muscles in quick succession as you use the come here motion to caress your g spot. Use breath work to slow down and build up the pleasure.

Whichever ways you decide to experiment, focus on the sensations and how they make you feel as you explore, what feels good for you? What areas of your body send shivers and gives goose bumps? Do you get more turned on with words or actions? This is an activity that should be fun and exciting, so forget any pre-conceived inhibitions and let the self-love flow.

Communication

Now that you have had time to explore your body and learn what sends you into a state of ecstasy you are ready to show up to your partner(s) and express your deepest sexual desires. Communication is essential when it comes to a fulfilled and satisfying sex life with your partner. It can be scary to open up at first, but clear communication will build trust, bring you closer together in all aspects of your relationship and save you from any unnecessary hurt or misunderstanding.

It took me a long time to understand this because I clearly did not trust anything anyone told me when it came to my body issues. I had no clue what my body needed to feel loved by me let alone anyone else and I certainly wasn't comfortable taking my clothes off, and articulating my desires to my partner for him to think badly of me hell no. I felt that sex was something I had to do every now and then to keep my partner happy, that was a women's job, right?

Women joke at the parties I do that they lay back and plan their shopping list or what they have to do the next day during sexual intercourse with their partners. This for me is very upsetting. It is clear that as women we are still living in the past, and sex is thought of as a duty rather than as an act of love. This is evident with the number of women that reach orgasm during sex being as low as 25%, no matter the size of his goods, how long sex lasts or how the woman feels towards the relationship even now in the 21st century this is the statistic. This needs to change don't you agree.

So, it is time for us to step up and take charge when it comes to our sexual fulfilment, and communication is key. I know it sounds cliché and you have heard this many times I'm sure but communication, especially around the things we want and desire within a relationship, is a necessity even if it is something that feels uncomfortable to do to start with. The reality here is if two people are not open and honest about their wants, needs and desires the relationship is likely to suffer or end eventually. As feelings of mistrust and jealousy will most certainly rear their ugly head, and this in turn will have you feeling unwanted, un-loved and not good enough, and yet the vicious circle of self-doubt and self-worth will continue.

We are on a mission to empower women across the world to become the highest version of themselves, to show up in all aspects of their lives as confident beautiful souls. Unleashing their inner diva and knowing that their wants, needs, and desires are just as valuable and meaningful as the next persons.

Do not be afraid to articulate what you want or do not want from your partner but remember this is a two-way street so take the time to listen to your partners wants, needs, and desires too. You will be surprised how similar they are to your own. Both of you will ultimately be wanting to please and pleasure the other, being open with them will likely bring you closer and help to build trust and respect for one another.

A technique I use with my clients when learning to connect with their partner more intimately is couple mindfulness and meditation. Meditation is a powerful practice and it trains our minds to focus on the present moment, quietening all the chatter and allowing us to consciously recognise what comes to the forefront of our minds, whilst allowing ourselves to acknowledge and let go of any stress and tension that is no longer serving us. It is a powerful practice to have in your toolbox whether you practice with or without a partner.

By practicing together, you are able to strengthen your relationship, and with continual practice you are able to tune into each other's subtle cues bringing harmony within your relationship. This is achieved through synced breath work, self-awareness, and a deeper connection. Meditation also helps you to feel less stressed and more relaxed which will bring a calming atmosphere into even the most stressful of days.

The great thing with meditation is there is no right or wrong way to practice, it can be done at any time of day, for any length of time, it can be self-led or guided, with or without music, indoors or outdoors, sitting up or lying down. The choice is yours. It is a great way for you and your partner to spend some time together just being present. You can sit facing each other or back to back. By making this part of your daily practice together you are showing true commitment in embracing a loving satisfying relationship and communicating on a deep level.

As well as practicing meditation, being mindful when together is a great way to communicate how you are feeling. Do you tentatively listen when your partner is telling you about their day, or are you running around after the kids or trying to cook up a storm in the kitchen? Do you eat meals together? Take walks holding hands together? And if so, are you present in those moments or is your mind wandering thinking about all you have yet to do before bed?

ACTIVITY THREE

It may have become apparent by now that communication is a key element in your sex life as well as in other areas too. It may also have become apparent that change does not just happen, and that it is down to you to take action. Yep that is right I said it is down to you. You are the creator of your life. You have the power to create the life you desire. You just have to make a conscious decision to take action.

Have you taken action on the other activities within this book or have you skimmed right past them? If you have, I urge you to start right here with this activity and then ensure you take the required action necessary to complete each activity provided for you. You will be pleasantly surprised how implementing these steps can start to really support you on your self-love journey.

Now for activity three.

Take some time to figure out how you can implement some of the communication skills provided above into your relationship. These do not have to be the big steps, you can start by being a little more mindful, next time your partner is telling you about their day stop what you are doing and listen. Make eye contact, show emotion, do not interrupt them with your own day or points of view as they speak, but listen attentively and take cues as to when to reply within the conversation.

Get into the habit of making the kids tea first and getting them off to bed so you can enjoy a meal together, cuddle up on the sofa with a movie and popcorn. Take a regular walk with the dog if needed and just be present in the moment.

Make a date night jar together, pop activities, places, and intimate moments you love to do together into a jar and pick one out at random. Aim to implement one mindful activity into your daily life right away. And then increase them as you master this skill. Before you know it, you will be sharing your deepest desires and having mind blowing sex as well as a life full of happiness and abundance.

Be a player not a spectator, all it takes is for one of you to start the journey to make it happen, So many of us do not know what it feels like to have a connection with our own sexual space. The exchanging of energy and connection has true power so step up as the empowered version of yourself and take charge of your destiny.

Partner Play

Why not surrender your body over to your partner, trust that they have your very needs at the fore front of their mind and that they get just as much pleasure from serving you as you do being served.

Allow yourself to be blindfolded to heighten your senses and let your partner go to town.

Maybe they start with gentle stroking of your hair as they whisper sweet nothings in your ear – our ears are filled with tiny nerve endings around the lobe and inside the ear sending highly sensitive vibrations through the ear canal with each word whispered. The bottom of the ear contains tons of nerve endings so gentle nibbling of the lobe can be a real turn on. Then maybe they move down your neck, as they do you can feel the sensation of their breath giving you goose bumps all over your body. Maybe they gently kiss and lick your neck.

For a second, they stop, and your mind starts to wonder what is coming next. It could be a tender kiss, the warmth of a body safe massage candle as the warm wax hits your chest or maybe even ice over your nipples, all 800 nerve endings enjoying the sensation before having them sucked, pulled or gently nibbled on.

Like I mentioned before stimulation of the nipples releases that happy hormone oxytocin and so by now your body is already in a state of pure bliss. Maybe you feel a feather gently caressing over your arms, neck, and back of the knees making its way up your thigh. Your inner thigh loves the feeling of fingertips and the tip of the tongue, bringing shivers of anticipation as your partner moves closer to that sweet spot. I will let your imagination take over from here.

The Power is Inside You

Has anyone ever told you, you are a mother f**king queen who deserves all she has ever dreamt of? Well if not I am telling you right now. No matter where or what you have been through in life it does not define you. You, yes you are a divine goddess, who has the right to feel empowered, sexy, and confident both in and out of the bedroom. Fact!

No one has the right to make you feel inferior, unloved, ugly, desexualised, or inadequate in any way. No one has that right, not even you. That life you dream of where you are happy, loved and have all that you ever wanted, it is right there for the taking. The power is already inside of you, trust me I know. I have suffered mental and physical abuse, felt inadequate, unloved, scared, ashamed, alone, unwanted, embarrassed, and unworthy at the hand of not only others but myself too.

I allowed those mind monkeys to play havoc with my mental health, suffering with severe anxiety and depression and body dysmorphia. I let myself be used by others in a mad attempt to fit in. I was that friend that always said yes, always showed up, the one who would put others needs and opinions before her own. I was afraid that if I voiced my own opinion I would be cast aside. I looked in the mirror every day and despised who I saw.

I had accepted that this was my life, I was not meant for a life filled with joy and happiness. Those dreams that I had to make a positive change, to feel beautiful and accepted, to enjoy an abundant sex life, the career, the perfect house, financial prosperity these were not for me, I was not deserving enough.

My daughter saved me, she showed me that only I had the power to show up as that higher version of me. If I wanted to make sure she and her siblings understood that their potential was limitless then I had to first prove this to myself. I had to step up and acknowledge that I am worthy, that I am deserving of all I have ever dreamed of, and so I began my journey. It has taken years for me to know my true worth, to understand that it is my own mindset that gets in the way of my achievements. It has taken me years to know it is okay to feel low sometimes, but it is how you deal with those lows that makes all the difference.

It has taken me years to learn I am deserving of the best people in my life, those that fill my cup with an abundance of love, light, and laughter. It has taken years of daily positive affirmations to ensure when those naughty mind monkeys creep in, I have the power to tell them to do one, because whatever they are saying I can't do or say, I know I can. And it has taken me many years to feel comfortable in my own skin both mentally and sexually.

But it wasn't until Adriano was diagnosed with terminal lung cancer in 2018 that I found my true power, a tool that not only helped my family look for the good in our current situation but one that gave me the realisation that even in the most difficult of situations there is hope. I found the power of gratitude. Yep here she goes again banging on about gratitude. But it really is the most powerful tool you can ever possess trust me.

The universe works in magical ways and when you can learn to trust in its power amazing things start to happen, trust that it has your back. Here we are as a family absolutely devastated having been told that Adriano has an incurable illness and boom a book on gratitude lands on my lap. If you have not read the Magic by Rhonda Byrne, I highly recommend it. It helped me work out where I wanted to go in life. Right at that moment the universe was showing us that if we did not change our ways, time was short.

Adriano worked on his mindset and the food he fuelled his body with, and I set to work ensuring we were showing up as best we could each and every day. We did not let this diagnosis slow us down. We continued to show up, make memories and live each day to its fullest. It taught us that we need to live in the moment. Set those intentions and take each day as it comes.

In the past eighteen months we have achieved mountains, Adriano has got this nasty disease just where he wants it, his mindset and willingness to try alternative therapies and eat foods he wouldn't dare have touched had kept the cancer at bay. I have become a best-selling author twice, with this being my third collaboration book. Three of my children have become bestselling authors. I set up a new business and Love Thy Body Project was born. I have addressed hundreds of women on stage alongside Caprice. I am surrounded by inspirational women who share my vision to empower others to become the most confident version of themselves. I hit Team Leader status within Ann Summers, something I had been trying to do for several years. I am showing up each day with gratitude at the fore front of my mind. Knowing that the universe, my friends, and those within the Love Thy Body Project community have my back just as I have theirs.

I am living a life of abundance each and every day. I have allowed myself to accept the power that is within me. To understand that other people's opinions of me only affect me if I let them. That I am capable and worthy of the life I choose to live. That it is okay to have hopes, dreams, and desires that are just outside of my comfort zone because when I push for them that is when I grow. I have learned that my body is mine and I can love it for what it is because it tells my story, my journey to true empowerment.

I understand that each and every one of us are beautiful, our scars and imperfections are what make us unique. If I were not me, I would not have those I love in my life. If I were not me, I would not have my beautiful children. If I were not me, I would not be here now, writing this book to support other women in finding their true power.

They say it takes a traumatic event to finally realise your true worth, well I have had a few of those for sure, so I want to ensure my knowledge to a happier, healthier, and sexually empowered version of me is out there to help women across the world.

ACTIVITY FOUR

This activity has been one of the most powerful tools I use both personally and with my clients. It is a tool to help you gain clarity on your goal's, dreams, and desires as well as realising just how far you have already come. As with all these activities there is no right or wrong way to completing this, but I am going to share with you my preferred way and one I feel helps you to really take hold of your power.

A DAY IN MY LIFE

Within this activity I want you to think ahead it can be six months, a year, or two years from now. I want you to visualise your ideal day. Where do you see yourself? What kind of house do you live in? Do you live in the country you are in right now or have you moved abroad? What kind of job do you have? Do you have children? Do you have a partner? What physical shape are you in? Are you a tiger in the bedroom? What car do you drive? Are you debt free? Who are you surrounded by? Do you have a nanny? A cleaner? A pool? Or do you live by the sea? What kind of clothes do you wear? How do you wear your hair? What kind of music do you listen to? What activities do you participate in? What colour wallpaper do you have in your home? What kind of sheets do you have on your bed?

I want you to really think about this, and then I want you to journal using as much detail as you can, map out a day in your perfect life. What do you hear the moment you open your eyes? How do the sheets feel on your skin? Are you waking up to make mad passionate sex? Or are you starting your morning with a little meditation? What can you hear as you move around the house, how do these sounds make you feel? Continue to write until you close your eyes at the end of the day. But as you finish, I want you to write "Thank you (insert your name) for the perfect day".

Let the words flow and let your imagination for your future self and those hopes, dreams, and desires run freely on the paper. When you are done, I want you to get two different coloured highlighters.

Use one of the highlighters to go through your day and highlight everything that is already in place right now that you have included in your day. It could be you already start your day with a nice cup of coffee, and that you are surrounded by your children. Whatever it is big or small make sure you highlight it. Then with you other highlighter I want you to go through the text and highlight things within your perfect day that you can start implementing right away. It could be that you love to dance, it could be that you have put you exercise daily, or that you sit down for a meal with your family every night. It could even be that you take time each day to spend with your partner doing something fun you both enjoy. So, what is stopping you? Highlight it and figure out how to implement that into you day right now.

So how much of your ideal day is left? When I did mine it became apparent that I was holding myself back on a lot of what I desired. And what shocked me was that most of it was easily implemented into my daily routine right away. Which then gave me the space to manifest and work towards the bigger dreams.

Once you have written this out and highlighted what you already have, and what you can implement now I would like you to record yourself saying your ideal day out loud. Pick a device like your phone so you can listen to it on a daily basis. Speak slowly and read out your ideal day exactly as you wrote it. Then ensure that you set time to listen to this daily, be it on your commute to work, whist getting ready in the morning or last thing at night. Our subconscious mind is like a sponge and recognises the sound of your own voice, so it is a powerful tool to help you change the way you think and feel. You will be manifesting that ideal day and telling your subconscious mind you are deserving of all the good in your life.

Final Thoughts

So, no matter why you chose to pick up this book, remember life really begins the moment you say yes and embrace the power inside. So, release the inner diva from within and shine like the empowered diamond you are.

I hope that you have taken inspiration from this book, that you are now feeling a little more confident in embracing the changes you need for your own personal self-love journey, whether that be through taking parts of each of the co-founder chapters or a specific chapter in general. Know that we have your back every step of way. When women come together to empower and lift each other up amazing things start to happen. It is my mission to spread the power of self-love across the globe to ensure that the next generation of women already have the tools in place so when their mind monkey starts to creep in they can chase her away. That they live their lives knowing they are worthy of all they desire from the very start. In buying this book you are making that happen. So, I want to thank you for stepping up, the co-founders of Love Thy Body Project are making waves but together we are creating a freaking tsunami.

Serena Novelli is a body confidence and sexual empowerment coach, founder of Love Thy Body Project brand, author and keynote speaker on a mission to empower women across the globe to feel confident and comfortable in their own skin.

Having five children Serena knows just how important it is to learnt o love who you are from the inside out. She offers a range of different packages to enable every woman to feel body confident.

You can find out more about Serena and Love Thy Body Project at www.lovethybodyproject.com

Lightning Source UK Ltd.
Milton Keynes UK
UKHW020637141222
413904UK00011B/1532